# THE HIDDEN PRINCE

# THE HIDDEN PRINCE

## (The Non-Royal ROYAL)

ROBERT GLASBURY

Riverside Publishing Solutions

Robert Glasbury has asserted his moral right to be identified as the author of this Work in accordance with the Copyright, Designs and Patents Act 1988.

ISBN: 978-1-913012-76-2

I would like to dedicate this book to my father,
Roy Albert and to his mother, my grandmother, Rose.
Without their past lives, this book would not have
been possible.

My father, Roy Albert, gave me his letters, including those from
King George V and the King's Private Secretary,
Clive Wigram, many years ago. He asked me many
times if I would write his life story in his own words
and have it published.

After years of research with the assistance from my wife,
Sue, my daughters, Ruth and Stephanie and the dedication
from my son-in-law, Mark, it came to resemble a book.

My father was very pleased with our achievements.
He insisted and made me promise that it would
not be published until after his death.

After his passing and my family time to grieve,
I feel this is the right time for publication.

*Robert Andrew*

# CONTENTS

# CONTENTS

# Chapter One

## MY MOTHER

I remember my mother slapping my face so hard, I did not think my ear would ever stop ringing. Four times a year a tall slender man in a dark suit wearing a bowler hat would visit the house. He would pull up in a big fancy car, park it on the road and with his head held high, walk towards the house in a military fashion. Mum knew this was the day for him to visit. "I want you all outside when he comes," mum said to dad, Jim, and I. "Outside and stay there until he has gone." It was a cold damp day, and I didn't want to go outside but I had no choice. "Get out" she yelled to the three of us, "come on now move."

The three of us went out of the backdoor, dad asked Jim to give him a hand with the wood. I stayed in the garden and looked over the wall towards the road. Dad and Jim started moving pieces of wood into the shed ready to cut into blocks. From the garden I could see a man in a round hat walking down the track and go towards the house. As soon as he entered the house through the front door, I ran to the window, climbing up to see if I could look in, but I could not see anything. I jumped down and moved towards the backdoor, Dad and Jim were occupied as they carried the wood into the shed. I gently turned the door handle and silently sneaked in. I could hear mum and the man talking. I tried to hide near the doorway but they both looked straight at me. "So, this is Edward, is it?" said the man. "Come here boy so I can see you," he continued. My mother looked at me sternly, so I knew what was to come later.

"So, you're Edward?" the man asked again. "No!" I replied, "My name is Roy, and I am six years old." The man smiled at me and looked at mum inquisitively. Mum told him "that I was now called Roy." The man handed mum an envelope and said he would see her again in four months' time and headed for the door.

When his car pulled away from the road, I asked mum who he was and why he gave her an envelope. I could see the rage in her face and then suddenly she slapped me. I burst out crying. "You can stop that right now" she erupted. As she leaned over me, gritting her teeth, she lowered her voice and said, "Just remember, the only thing you will ever be is Arthur's son." I did not understand what any of that meant, I walked towards the backdoor and dad came into the house. "What are you doing in here boy!" he asked. "Mum just hit me," I replied. Dad slapped me across the head and growled "Get out boy, get out." I ran into the garden crying; Jim came over and he also began telling me off. "Why did you go in the house?" he moaned. "I wanted to see what was going on that's all, that man called me Edward, I told him my name is Roy. Why would he call me Edward?" I cried. "Mum hit me and then when I told dad, he hit me too." Jim calmed me down and said, "Look, I can't tell you what is going on right now but when you are a bigger boy, I will tell you then." "I am big!" I replied to Jim. "I am six!" Jim was twelve years old, nearly thirteen. "Why don't we go and throw sticks in the water?" he asked, so that is what we did.

My mother, Rose Elizabeth Mary Davies, was born in 1904. Her parents, my granny and grandad, were named James and Elizabeth Davies. Mum was one of two daughters; her sister was named Ellen May but was always known as May.

Granny and grandad farmed a place called Huntless Farm when the girls were small. Grandad worked the farm and also did contract work for other farms in the area, so he could earn extra money to save to buy a farm of their own. Granny taught the girls to keep house from an early age. Cooking, cleaning, sewing, and mending. My mother, Rose, was very good at keeping house while May was more of an outside girl, although she did do her share of duties in the house. Both girls were taught if you want something, you work hard for it, that you can have anything and everything if you work hard.

A few years later, granny, grandad and the girls moved from Huntless Farm to the Lawns, a small farm that they had saved for with the extra work he did, proving hard work and saving can get you what you want. Granny continued teaching the girls. She taught them to read and write, hoping that one day with their good manners and household skills they would both find good husbands.

Rose had a temper and was quite argumentative. Her tongue was razor sharp and on many occasions, this did her no favours. May, on the other hand, was quiet and shy. I found she would only speak if spoken to first, otherwise, she would just sit there observing the atmosphere. The family found this annoying, and often Rose would shout at her. They were not close sisters but tolerated one another. When mum was in her 20s, she wanted to find a husband. There were not many suitors as men were few and far between. She met a farmer named Fred, who was a tenant on a farm. They married very quickly in their relationship, my mother then moved to Brook Farm with Fred, and later Jim was born. Jim was my older half-brother. I got the impression from mum that she was not happy at Brook Farm. Fred was a rugged kind of man, not many manners to speak of and he was twice mum's age. Mum was 22 years old; Fred was 45, and they did not have any shared interests. Mum kept house as best as she could on the money earned, things were very tight, and this was not something mum was used to. Fred was quite a poorly man he suffered from chest infections and headaches quite often. Mum soon got fed up with this and told him to pull himself together. Fred had a brother Leonard, who would come to the farm and help whenever Fred was unwell. There was also a farm employee and an elderly man who would help in exchange for cooked meals. Mum would often say she wanted more than this in life, but there was nowhere for her to go. Grandad was a kind and fair man, he told mum that her place was to look after her husband, do the best she could with what she had. Mum did not like that response, as she felt she was better than that.

**Rose Davies**

# Chapter 2

# AN UNEXPECTED DEATH

On Saturday morning Fred not feeling well, left the house to go to work on the farm. Although he did not have the strength to complete the normal jobs that were supposed to be done, he decided to walk around and check the livestock. Leonard had come to visit, which he had so often done, he went to the furthest field on the farm to check the fencing and the livestock. On the way back to the house, he noticed the sheepdog standing near the brook. He called the dog, but the dog's attention was set in the brook. Leonard continued calling while walking towards the dog, he then discovered his brother Fred, lying on his back in the brook with his head under the water. Instead of pulling his brother out of the water, he ran back to the farmhouse to tell Rose. This was something that haunted my mother for the rest of her life. That day, the Doctor had called by to see Fred. Leonard told the Doctor that Fred was in the brook, and he had come to the house to get help. Dr Strange, Leonard and the elderly helper went to where Fred was in the brook. Dr Strange told them to move Fred out of the water and for one of them to head to the village and bring the Policeman on duty. When the Police Officer arrived, Dr Strange told them that Fred had died of drowning and that no foul play was involved.

Rose was upset and could think of nothing but the funeral and where her and Jim, were going to live. Mum told me years later she was upset with hearing the news that Fred had drowned, but not as heartbroken as most people thought she should be.

Below is the transcript of the obituary from the Hereford Times.

## TRAGIC DISCOVERY
## BIRCH FARMER DEAD IN A BROOK
## JURY'S VERDICT

*A tragic discovery was made at the
Callow, Much Birch, near Hereford
on Saturday, when the body of
Mr Frederick James Jones of Brook Farm
was found in a stream which is
known as Red Brook.
Mr Jones who had a small farm, had
been under the care of Dr Strange, of
Hereford. He was last seen alive that
morning at about 10 o'clock. About an
hour later he was dead His body was
found laying in the Red Brook.
Dr Strange had attended the deceased on
Friday evening and advised him to go to
bed. The Doctor called again on Saturday
and then heard the tragic news that his
patient had been found dead, Mr Jones
was married about two years ago.*

### THE INQUEST

*At the inquest, held by Mr E. L. Wallis,
coroner for South Herefordshire, and a jury,*

*at the Ridgehill Mission Room,
Lower Bullingham, on Monday evening evidence
was given by Mr John Jones, of Baristree,
small-holder, brother-in-law of the deceased,
that on Saturday and preceding days he had
been at the Brook Farm to give assistance.
His brother-in-law was suffering from a cold
and slight bronchitis and had complained of
pains in the head. On Saturday morning the
deceased had breakfast as usual and later
about 10 o'clock he had a little lunch and
then went out again on farm duties.
Witness also went out to a different part
of the farm and about an hour later
accompanied by a sheep dog whose "setting"
caused him to look into the Brook. He there
saw his brother-in-law laying in two feet
of water on his back with his feet on the bank.
There were no signs of a struggle, but there
were marks on the bank that might have been
caused by someone slipping. Witness ran to the
house for assistance. There was a flush of water
in the Brook due to Friday's rain. "He was the
last to do anything of this kind," said the witness.
Matthew Cooke aged 82, farm labourer, said that
he helped the previous witness to get the body out
of the brook. At that time Dr Strange had just
called at the house to see Mr Jones and on being
told of the discovery the Doctor went with them to
the brook. "He told us to pull him out" said the
witness, and we did so. The Doctor examined him
and said he was dead. We knew that. Witness
added that a Policeman was sent for and the body*

*was taken on a stretcher to the house.*

## EVER SO HAPPY

*Mrs Rose Elizabeth Mary Jones, widow of the
deceased said he was 45 years of age, and they were
married in 1926. Her husband had no financial
trouble or trouble otherwise, except the cold and
slight bronchitis. He had not been depressed.
He was ever so happy with his little boy and all,
she said the boy was nine months old.
Dr. Strange gave evidence that on the Friday he
advised Mr Jones to go to bed and stay there until
he saw him the next day. On Saturday morning he
called on his rounds and was told of the discovery.
He went to the place and examined the body. There
were no marks of violence and death had been caused
by drowning. It was possible that Mr Jones might
have felt faint when crossing the brook to go to one of
his men who was working in a field, and have fallen in
such a way as to have been stunned.
In this case he would be helpless.
The Jury found a verdict of "Accidental Death"
adding that the deceased died from drowning and that
he probably slipped into the brook when crossing it.*

# Chapter 3

## GOODBYE BROOK FARM

Rose packed what she was taking from the house at Brook Farm, there was not a lot, 2 suitcases and a small box. The large dresser which Jim slept in the bottom drawer, Rose could not take, as Leonard had said all the furniture had been given to him by Fred. Rose was not in the right frame of mind to argue with Leonard, so she let him keep all of the furniture. My granny and grandad, Elizabeth, and James, came and collected my mother, Jim and her possessions. They all left for the Lawns on their horse and cart, this was to be her new home from now on. Rose was unsettled and wanted more out of life, she felt that she had taken a step backwards by moving in with her parents.

The following day, Elizabeth asked Rose if she would like to go to the market with her; Anything to get Rose out of the house to stop her grieving. At the market many of the local people paid their respects to Rose for the loss of Fred. One of the locals known as Arthur Powell, quite short and skinny, not much to look at, approached Rose. He said he was sorry to hear that her husband had died in a most awkward manner. He then went on to say to Rose how he had met King George. "The good old King himself!" Arthur said enthusiastically. "How?" Rose asked. "I was one of the beaters on a shoot, I picked up some birds and was told to take them over to the third man, when I got there, it was the King." Arthur replied. Rose wanted to hear more but her mother called her, and she had to leave. "Will I see you again?" Arthur asked. Rose replied with one word from her lips, "Maybe!" as she walked away with her mother through the market.

On the way home, Rose told Elizabeth what Arthur had told her, how he met the King. Elizabeth looked at Rose and snapped, "now don't go getting any fancy ideas, you have only just lost Fred and you have Jim to think about." For the next few weeks, Rose went to the market by herself to do the shopping hoping to find Arthur. She looked out for him each time, but he was not there. As she was on her way home, a horse and cart passed by. On the back of the cart was Arthur, he was sat with one of his brothers. He jumped off the cart, "I'll catch you up" he shouted to his brother in the distance as he carried on.

"How are you Rose?" Arthur asked. "Where have you been? Not seen you at market for a while!" Rose replied. Arthur continues, "No, I am on the shoots, I've done with the others, more than four now and seen the King and his party on nearly everyone. He doesn't speak to me unless I get him his birds, but I make sure he knows I am there. He's a wonderful old fellow, I really like him". Rose replied in disbelief, "As if you know our King, you're so full of it!" Arthur responded, "I know a lot of staff at the palaces, a Footman, a Butler, and several Maids. They all talk and tell me lots of gossip, the things I can tell you, well." Rose began walking towards home, with a smirk, she playfully remarked, "Well, suppose I must get on. Will I see you next week or are you dining with the King?" "I am off again on Tuesday, so don't think I will see you next week, but I will let you know when I am back. Bye Rose, bye," Arthur answered.

Rose thought about the King and London all the way home with so many thoughts swirling around her head about how she wanted more than this. After a week of moving irritably around and complaining about everything, Rose wrote to Buckingham Palace asking if any sewing work was available, now or in the near future. As time passed, no reply was sent to Rose. She continued working from home, taking in repairs and alterations to make some money to pay her way.

# Chapter 4

# INTERVIEW INVITATION

It was in the December of 1932 when a letter was delivered to the farm offering Rose an interview at Buckingham Palace. Rose couldn't believe what she was reading. Not knowing how her family would react, Rose explained to her parents and May, the letter she had received and if it was possible for her to go to the interview. At first, James was completely against it and said no. James challenged her that she should find another husband and settle down. Elizabeth knew if Rose did not go to London, living with her and her self-pity would be a nightmare. Elizabeth spoke to May about it and said that they would let her go and May would look after Jim. Rose could not find the words to express her gratitude, all she could think about was going for the interview. On the Wednesday morning, Rose was up early and ready to go to market. She was desperate to see Arthur and tell him the news about the interview.

When Rose arrived at the market, she could not find Arthur, but his brother, Frank, was there. In Rose's eyes, Frank was the more handsome one out of the brothers. He was quiet and had the most piercing eyes and that was something Rose liked. She asked him "where was Arthur?" "Arthur has gone on the shooting party again," Frank replied. He continued, "He loves it and earns a fair bit of money, anything to get away from the Maypole." Rose interjected, "I'm off to London myself. I have an interview for my sewing."

"You watch yourself," Frank pleaded. "Those city folk aren't like us. They're fast and wild in the stories our Arthur comes out with, well, most of it he says shouldn't be allowed in any society. Just watch yourself." Rose continued buying the things she needed and began the long walk home. All the way Rose was hoping that someone would pass by with a horse and cart, so she could ask for a lift on the back, but not today. She did not see a single person and continued walking all the way home along the long winding, deserted country lane.

When Rose arrived home, she told Elizabeth and May, who she had seen at the market and showed them what she had bought. "Nothing for Jim," Elizabeth expressed. Jim needed new shoes, and was growing out of his clothes, so Rose was asked to make something. Begrudgingly, she said that she would make it out of an old shirt of her dad's. As the days passed, Rose became more and more excited. She packed her sewing samples and embroidery samples into her small case, "Should I take an overnight case?" She stated grandly. Elizabeth replied, "What the hell for? You are only going for an interview. There's no promise of a job and who will look after Jim, if you do get the job? May and I have enough to do, so think on."

# Chapter 5

# FROM HEREFORD TO LONDON

It was the morning of the interview. Rose was up bright and early waiting for the sunrise to catch up. She cleaned out the fire ready for lighting, something she would only occasionally do as it was a dirty job. It was always left for May to do. Rose made a pot of tea and put the eggs on to boil for breakfast. Soon after, James, Elizabeth and May were at the table. "What's going on here then? You should have an interview more often if this is what it does for you." James said as he chuckled. They continued to eat their breakfast. Rose moaned, "Don't wake Jim until I have left for the train, as you know he will want to come and I'm not in the mood for that this morning." She went upstairs to get changed into her Sunday best, this consisted of a dress and jacket that she had made herself. It was tailored to fit her, hugging her womanly curves perfectly and she looked stunning in it. Always a head-turner when she wore it to church, or in fact, when Rose wore the two-piece suit anywhere. Her slim figure, her shoulder length hair which she had curled with rags, so it turned under and sat on her shoulders. She had polished her leather shoes until they gleamed.

Ready to go, Rose said her goodbyes to her mother and sister and was off. Her father took her to the train station so she could catch the early morning train, this gave her plenty of time to get to London. Rose could see the train pulling into the station when she was hit with a bout of nerves and stumbled a little, as she approached the door of the train carriage. She saw a couple down the platform pull open the door of the carriage and Rose did the same. She climbed in, holding her ticket close to her chest. She closed the door behind her and sat down staring at the seat opposite and began to panic wondering whether she should sit facing the direction of travel or backwards. She sat with her back towards the front of the train so she could see Hereford station as she was leaving, heading towards the big city. As the train pulled away from the station, it jolted, she jumped out of her seat, this startled the other passengers in the carriage. She then changed her seats so she could see the landscape out of the window getting closer and closer. She lifted her small case from the overhead rack and placed it on the seat next to her.

Ten minutes into the journey, the Ticket Inspector entered Rose's carriage. Enthusiastically, Rose handed the Ticket Inspector her ticket. He punched a hole into it and while handing the ticket back, he explained, "You need to keep this one for your journey home Miss." Rose took the ticket, thanking him and gushed, "I'm going to London." The Ticket Inspector chuckled, "I know, I punched your ticket." Rose continued, "I'm going to Buckingham Palace." The Ticket Inspector smiled, "To see the King miss?" No! "I've got an interview at the Palace," replied Rose. As the Ticket Inspector moved on, he wished her luck. Rose sat back, absorbing where she was and what she was experiencing, on a train for the first time, with the feeling of the padded seat beneath her which felt coarse and fluffy. The experience of being independent and travelling was an exhilarating feeling and she could definitely see herself travelling more often on the train.

The train pulled into Newport Station, this was where Rose had to make a change, for the connecting train to London. She stepped off the train, not knowing where to go to get the next train, she began panicking and asked a Railway Porter for help. He took her to the platform and waited with her to make sure she boarded the next train to London. Rose felt very excited as the train pulled into the station, the Porter helped Rose on-board and carried her bag to her seat. The whistle blew and the train was in motion. She waved goodbye to the Station Master who waved back with a smile on his face.

# Chapter 6

# AN ANT AMONGST GIANTS

Rose eventually arrived in London; she was holding the money she had saved in her hand. Approaching a waiting taxi, she told the driver that she would like to go to Buckingham Palace. The taxi drove through street after street and Rose had never seen anything like it before. So many cars and so many people, they were everywhere. As the taxi moved into another street, there would be a new feeling of amazement, seeing shops of grandeur. The driver could definitely see that this was her first time in the big city, with her look of awe. Approaching Buckingham Palace the driver broke her focus, "Here we are Miss, this is Buckingham Palace, off to see the King, are you?" he asked. "No" she said, "I am here for an interview." Rose exited the taxi, with the money held tightly in her hand she passed it to the driver, whilst gazing up at the biggest building she had ever seen.

Rose slowly walked to the side of the building, she knocked on the door. She waited there for a few minutes contemplating whether to knock again. The door opened and was answered by a young girl. Rose introduced herself and explained she was there for an interview. The young girl told Rose to follow her, she would take her to the Housekeeper. Rose followed the Maid to a modest room with a small fire heating it. She stood in the centre holding her handbag and her case filled with her samples. a middle-aged woman came to meet her. "So, you're here for the sewing job, what's your name?" she asked. "My name is Rose Davies" Rose croaked. "Right. Well, you will be called Davies while you are here. We don't use anything other than surnames," the Housekeeper added. Rose acknowledged and accepted the rules of the names.

Rose was shown to the sewing room where she was introduced to a girl named Hughes, and an older looking girl named Lewis, both were there to sew and mend. They had a title of something of the wardrobe, but Rose could not remember what this was exactly, she found this very amusing. She showed them her samples that she had travelled with from home, which both women found impressive. Rose was then asked to do samples of her embroidery and also different mending stitches, which she did without hesitation. She was excited to see the treadle sewing machine as she had only used a hand turning machine at home. Rose asked Lewis and Hughes if she could have a go at using the sewing machine which they agreed to. She sat at the machine and was given a piece of fabric and set it up being careful not to make any mistakes. She pressed the foot pedal which first pulled the fabric back, and then it shot forward and gathered the fabric into a knot, which caused Hughes and Lewis to laugh. "Oh" Expressed Rose. "It's harder than it looks until you get used to it" Lewis cackled. Lewis stepped in, "Right, you can have another go. I will show you first and then you can take over from me." Lewis put the fabric onto the machine, placed it under the sewing foot and slowly moved the treadle wheel. It went back a little and then she applied a bit of pressure and it moved forward and started sewing. Lewis soon picked up speed and sewed the fabric in half the time you could do it with a hand-turning machine. Rose was very impressed and wanted to jump in and give it another shot, to rectify the mistake of her first go. She sat at the machine and copied the movements that Lewis had just performed and mastered it within a few minutes. Rose could not stop beaming with excitement saying she wanted one of those machines. Lewis and Hughes seemed to like Rose and said they would let her know if there was a position for her as they had to speak to others higher up the chain. Rose left her interview and was accompanied to the back gate. As she left, she stood for a moment by the fence gazing at the Palace. She was trying to comprehend what she had just experienced. It amazed her in so many ways.

On the way back to the train station, she began thinking about working and having a position at the Palace, how this would change her life; But if there was no employment for her, a treadle sewing machine would be the answer to her prayers. Rose gazed at the people moving along the streets. The way the ladies walked, as if they were gliding across ice in their fancy shoes. They were dressed very different to the two-piece she was wearing, which she had made herself. They were tailored, the length of the skirts and dresses were shorter than Rose's, not too much but were definitely above the ankle by at least three inches. Many of the women were wearing a dead animal around their neck. Rose was amazed by the different way of city life and the dressing she was witnessing and was personally against wearing such a thing. There was one lady she remembers vividly, the lady who stepped out of a taxi wearing a beautiful full-length fur coat. Rose had never ever seen such quality or class ever in her life.

Rose arrived back at the station and was waiting for her train to take her home. Other people were moving around, and waiting, as if they had been on a similar purpose to her. As the train came rolling into the station, she was still dreaming about the people she had just met and how they must live in this big city. She was desperate to keep a firm grip on her ambitions to improve her life. She stepped into her carriage and saw a man in a tweed suit, wearing a flat cap, accompanied by his young daughter who looked twelve or thirteen years old. The gentleman stood as Rose sat down and offered to put her case up on the overhead rack. Rose had a smile as wide as her face and began asking the young girl, "Have you had a nice day?" "I've just finished school and daddy is taking me home. I'm Jenny," she replied. Rose held out to her hand and Jenny shook her hand, "My name is Rose. I have just been to Buckingham Palace." The father joined in with the conversation at that point, "Did you meet the King?" he asked. "No." Said Rose, "everyone has asked me that this morning. I went for a position at the Palace." "What for? a secretary, assistant, cook, maid?" Jenny marvelled. Rose replied, "No, a seamstress. I am very good at sewing and wanted to take this opportunity to go for it." Rose began telling them about her day from start to finish leaving out no detail of what she had seen and done. Jenny and her father could see the excitement overflowing from her appearance. They sat back listening to her stories until they arrived at their destination.

# Chapter 7

# IT'S TIME TO CHANGE

When she arrived at Hereford train station, Rose picked up her case and got off the train. She could not see her father; this did not bother her as it meant that her day had not yet finished. As she left the station and began walking towards home, Rose saw her father approaching with the horse and cart. She ran over to him to tell him her stories about Buckingham Palace, and how different life in London was to Hereford. The stories continued all the way home without a break. When Rose got close to the house, she ran in to tell her mother and sister. Her father knew that things for Rose had changed, and that they would never be the same for her again whilst living in Hereford.

Rose sat at the table for tea, still in her best clothes, she was going on about how city life was everything, to Elizabeth and May. They could tell she was excited. Jim came rushing in to see his mummy, he wanted to give her a hug, as he had missed her. He had been out playing on the farm, and as he held out his hands, Rose could see they were dirty and pushed him away, "No Jim, not now, I'm in my best clothes. I will hug you later!" she muttered. Jim turned to May in tears and was welcomed by her with arms open wide, May comforted Jim saying, "what were you doing outside? Making mud pies? Let's go and see them." May followed Jim outside, leaving Elizabeth, Rose, and James in the house. Elizabeth turned to Rose and snapped, "You have been gone all day, you didn't see Jim this morning and have no time for him now." Rose leapt from her chair accusing them all of ruining her day while storming upstairs. Elizabeth ranted, "She couldn't even give the boy a hug, I don't know what she is really like," James looked at Elizabeth and resonated her anger. "I don't think any good will come if she gets the job." "I hope she doesn't get the bloody job!"

Upstairs, Rose was lying on the bed thinking of what her life could be like; London, the streets, the buildings, the people, how they dressed and how they spoke. Rose wanted more, more than living on the farm and more than going to market. She knew that there was a different life for her, and she was the only one who could change that.

The next day, Rose dressed in her work clothes and made her way downstairs. May had already lit the fire, "It's your turn to clean out the hen house" May told Rose, "And Jim needs to go to school." "Why haven't you taken him?" Rose scowled. "I have my own jobs to do, and dad wants me to help him outside today, why? What do you have planned with your time? You had yesterday off as it is, do your work and don't forget to take your son to school!" May yelled. Rose was not happy, shouting upstairs to Jim to get up, and get ready for school. Jim came down half-dressed and not wanting to go to school as his belly was hurting. Rose looked at him and told him to go back upstairs to bed and that she would bring a drink up for him. Jim moved towards his mother wanting a cuddle, but Rose was having none of it and sent him straight up to bed.

Elizabeth came in from collecting the eggs from the henhouse. "Didn't take you long getting Jim to school Rose." Said Elizabeth. "Jim's not feeling well so I sent him back up to bed." Rose responded. The anger built up in Elizabeth until she erupted, "Too bloody lazy to take your own child to school, hell Rose, May looks after him better than you." Rose poured a glass of milk and took it up to Jim. Jim demanded, "can I have a cuddle mum," but she rejected his cry for a hug and told him he was too big for that. As Rose went back downstairs, she heard her mother telling her father that she had not taken Jim to school, and that she was begrudging him as a son. James told Elizabeth to leave it for the time being as he had hoped that things would settle in a day or two, her ideas and dreams are too big for her life. Shocked from what she was hearing, Rose sat on the stairs to listen some more. "I think deep down she is glad Fred is dead and she certainly doesn't want the boy," James remarked. With that, Rose burst into the room deflecting, "That's not right, not right at all. Just because I'm not living in the past doesn't mean I am wrong. I took one day off and now you think I am useless. Well, there's nothing wrong with wanting to better yourself." James stood up warning Rose, "If you ever talk to us like that again, you and your boy can find somewhere else to live. You are no different to the rest of us." Rose disagreed, "Didn't you and mum always teach us that, we can be anything we want, go anywhere we wanted to, if we worked hard enough for it." Elizabeth jumped in, "You both need to calm down. Shouting will only upset Jim. Now Rose, there's nothing wrong with dreaming of going to London and having a different kind of life, but while you are living here, you need to help around the house and do more sewing and alterations, to bring in a bit of extra money." "Well, it isn't as though you and dad are short of anything are you, but I know I need to pay my way." Rose quipped.

When tensions had cleared, Rose asked her mother if she had any thoughts of changing her life. Elizabeth responded "No, you, May and your father are all that I have ever needed. Your father is a good man, a hard worker and has a kind heart."

Rose jested, "Aye and a bloody temper." Elizabeth concluded "He's never raised a hand to me or you girls. Never. Yes, he will raise his voice, but he has never lashed out. How many times have you yelled at Jim and then given him a good hiding?" Rose sheepishly looked at her mother, and to change the subject, asked if she should make a cup of tea.

Rose went to the backdoor and called out to her sister, "May, I have made you a cup of tea, come in and I can tell you about London." May sniggered, "What, you mean you have left out a bit of detail from yesterday? All you have spoken about since getting home is London." May washed her hands and sat down at the table. "Well, if you don't want to know then I won't bother," Rose whined. Elizabeth looked at May and rolled her eyes. "Alright then" said May, "start at the beginning." Rose began telling the story about the ride to the train station, the carriage in which she sat and the Ticket Inspector, describing as many details as she could remember. May and Elizabeth drank their tea, pretending to be interested. "What happens if you get the job?" May asked. "Will you be taking Jim with you? Where will he go to school? Who will look after him when you are working?" she continued. Rose was getting wound up by everything May was saying, and snapped, "Oh here you go May, ruining everything for me before it even starts. Well, I haven't got an answer for any of it, but I tell you what, I am not going to end up an old maid like you." May and Elizabeth were bemused but Rose continued, "What have you got going for you May? No looks to speak of, no class and no style. At least I want something more out of life than staying here and farming." May left the table with tears streaming down her face and turned to Rose blubbering, "You're your own worst enemy Rose. You have no idea about life at all." May stormed out of the house to go back to helping out on the farm.

Rose was sat at the table reflecting on what she had said to May, and how May had responded. Elizabeth remarked "That was mean, was there any need to go that far with May? You know that she will be upset for weeks, you had better say sorry before your father comes in or you will be in for it." With all the commotion Jim came downstairs to see what was happening. "Granny, what's with the shouting?" he asked. "It's alright," "Your mother and aunty May were at it again, nothing serious. How are you feeling." Jim did not reply, but asked "Can I stay up and go out to play?" Elizabeth looked at him bewildered, "I thought you were feeling unwell and that's why you didn't want to go to school?" "I wanted to stay home to see mum, as I didn't see her yesterday. She doesn't want to see me though and won't give me any cuddles granny." After hearing that, Elizabeth threw her arms around him and held him close. "You can always have a cuddle off me, and aunty May." "Now you go outside and play, make sure you put your coat and hat on, as I don't want you catching a chill. You have to go to school tomorrow and I will be taking you myself."

# Chapter 8

# EAGERLY WAITING

Day after day, Rose waited eagerly for the post to arrive. She would rush to the gate when the Postman turned up on his bicycle, but he greeted her with the same three words, "nothing today Rose." This went on for three long weeks. One morning, May collected the post from the Postman at the gate. The Postman told May that there was an important letter for Rose, was it the one she was waiting for, as it was marked from London. May took the post into the house, she gave the letters to Elizabeth, but held on to the one for Rose. "It's here Rose, it's here," Screamed May. Rose came rushing in and snatched the letter out of May's hand. Rose held the letter not knowing if it was good or bad news, she took in a deep breath. "I think I will open it in my room in case it is bad news." Elizabeth and May looked at Rose. "Bad news! It's about a job, not a death, pull yourself together Rose," Elizabeth replied. Rose opened the letter and quickly read it aloud for the walls in her bedroom to hear; "An interview has been arranged for you as a position is available for a short time to work on a specific project." The date and time were on the letter. Rose couldn't contain her excitement, rushing downstairs and dancing around May and Elizabeth in the sitting room. Repeating the words in the letter, time and time again, with her voice becoming higher pitched leading to the end of the letter. Elizabeth and May said nothing but gave each other long stares. Rose stopped to plan everything in her head of how she was going to go to the market the following day to tell everyone, especially Arthur Powell, who she hadn't seen for a long time. She could not wait to know what he would think as he was on the shoots getting the birds for King George. Rose could not believe her good new fortune; To be in Buckingham Palace, to work for the King, to be in London, and to do something she really enjoyed. Elizabeth intervened by saying, "Don't get your hopes up, you need to tell your father first. Have you thought about who will look after Jim and do your chores? There's so much to consider before you start thinking of going to London. I will speak to your father first and see what he says, I will try and smooth the way before you say anything to him." Rose thanked her mum for her support and went back up to her room.

The following morning, Rose was up bright and early, she lit the fire and got breakfast ready before anybody else had awoke. After breakfast Rose changed ready for town and went out to the stable yard. "Mum, are you coming to market this morning?" Rose asked. "Yes, and your father is coming too. Just hang on a moment while I tack up the horse." Rose was ready to go, dressed to impress, she went into the house to pick up her purse. As Rose was leaving the house, Elizabeth whispered to Rose, "Your father knows, and he is not happy. I would keep things quiet for the moment as we are going to the market together." Rose knew that she didn't want her parents to ruin her plans, so she kept quiet on the journey to the market. All she could think about were the thoughts racing around in her mind, and what Arthur's reaction would be. She walked around the market, weaving between the stalls and the people, looking at each and every face hoping to see Arthur's. Her head was swaying from side to side looking for Arthur, but she couldn't see him. Rose suddenly stopped, she could see Frank, Arthur's brother, and ran over to him. Frank was looking at the things for sale on a stall, and before Rose could open her mouth, he said, "Arthur is about here somewhere Rose." Rose smiled and thanked Frank, she looked up and saw Arthur just a few stalls away. She walked over to him with the biggest smile on her face. "Are you still seeing the King?" she asked. "No." he replied, "The shooting and beating has finished but I will see if they want me next season." Rose chirped, "I am going to work in Buckingham Palace where they live so I might see them all the time, not running around outside chasing birds like a dog." "Rose, London is not a safe place, why do you want to go there?" he asked. Rose was annoyed with Arthur, "I want to be better than I am here. I want to make something of my life. I want something better than this. This is nothing compared to what I will be doing." Arthur was irritated by the way Rose was behaving, "What, you think going into service, being a maid, is better than what you have got here? You need your head read. I am sure your father is not going to let you go," he ranted. Anger was building up within Rose until she burst, "I am not going to be a maid!" she yelled. "I will not be in service, I will be a seamstress, doing sewing on the Royal clothes, not picking up stinking birds like you! And don't say a damn word to my mother or father!" Rose couldn't take Arthur's reaction and stormed off to find her mother. "Did you find Arthur?" Elizabeth asked. Rose was still furious and told her mother how she saw him, and that she did not like him anymore because of his response to her news. Rose was being mean about the way Arthur looked, his jacket a size or two smaller than he was, he needed a haircut and was not what she wanted.

Elizabeth was about to tell Rose to watch her tongue when the Vicar and his wife passed by. As the Vicar doffed his cap to wish Elizabeth and Rose a good morning,

Rose approached the Vicar, "Good morning, Vicar," she said, "I have a letter from Buckingham Palace. I am going for another interview." The Vicar's wife was very impressed and asked Rose to tell her more about it. Rose began telling her about her visit to London, from the train journey there and back, the first interview, without missing any detail and everything in between. Time had passed and Rose was still telling her story. The market was becoming quieter and quieter with people leaving to carry on with their day when Elizabeth had to interrupt, "Come on Rose" she said, "Your father is waiting." Rose wanted to continue with her story when the Vicar's wife wished her luck and said her goodbyes. Rose and Elizabeth hurried down the street to James and they got on the cart, they could see he wasn't happy, and then he erupted, "Where the hell have you been? I wanted to leave an hour ago." The journey home was a quiet one, the only thing you could hear was the creaking of the wheels turning. No small talk was going to break the tension with every response from James being a snappy one-word answer. Rose was sat there thinking about the way Arthur had insulted her ambition. The one person she thought would be the happiest for her, knowing that he himself had worked for the king.

The next day, Rose was sorting clothes ready to take to London, questions were exploding in her mind every few seconds. Why is it another interview and not the position offered? why did it say in the letter that it is only for a short time? She couldn't figure it out, but it didn't stop her from packing everything she could think of. She remembered Hughes and Lewis the two ladies she met in her first interview; they were wearing clothes that were provided by the Palace. She was not sure if they would provide a uniform if the job were for a short time, so she carefully looked through every item of clothing that fitted. Rose had to tailor some of her own clothes to fit and look smart for her newfound position. May was downstairs getting herself ready to head out, when she yelled out to Rose, "I will pick up Jim on the way home as I will be at a farm near the school, is that alright with you Rose?" There was no response from Rose, as her mind was wedged deep in Buckingham Palace.

Later that afternoon, Rose had a visitor, Arthur Powell. Rose approached him biting her tongue with crossed arms, she was vexed with him. "I'm sorry for what I said to you Rose. I could see I upset you and I didn't mean to do that. Would you like to go for a walk with me?" Arthur grovelled. Before Rose could say anything that she had to say to Arthur, Elizabeth disrupted the tension, "That sounds like a good idea, a nice long walk will do you both good." Without saying a word, Rose exhaled loud for them all to hear and picked up her jacket, walked by Arthur, and turned towards him as if she had been waiting for him this whole time.

They were both walking side by side and Arthur was telling Rose what was happening at the Maypole. The Maypole was the farm where Arthur, his sister, Ada Elsie (known as Elsie), Frank, and his two younger brothers lived. "It sounds boring, Arthur. Don't you miss London?" she asked. "I wasn't in London," he replied, "I was at Sandringham, and I run for birds. I only got the job because they were short and needed help. It wasn't an important job, but I did talk to King George, and I did meet staff that had come from London. They were different to you and I, they speak differently from the first word that leaves their mouth and they do different things. They are really not like us Rose, so, I am telling you, you have to be careful, especially living in such a big house with all the staff, men, and women." Rose could not help but laugh, "It's not a big house, it's a Palace and I can't wait to go there." Arthur was thinking of things to say that would change

Rose's mind. "I have heard you can't work there if you are married or having children. Who's going to look after your son, Jim?" He quizzed Rose. Rose did not respond and continued walking, picking up the pace. Arthur looked puzzled and skipped to catch up with Rose. "You haven't told them about Jim, have you?" He asked. "So, they don't know?" With no response still from Rose, Arthur continued, "I bet you haven't told them you were married before, have you?" Arthur kept pestering Rose until she finally responded. "No, I haven't told them. They said that I am to be called by my maiden name, Davies, so that is what they will call me. I did not have to tell them my name is Jones, and that I have a child, as no one asked me. So, I didn't." Arthur couldn't believe Rose hid that information from them. "What will your mother and father think of that? Do you think they would still let you go if they knew you kept that information from the staff at the Palace? Think of how much shame that would bring on your family if you were dismissed from the Palace." Rose stopped Arthur in his tracks and confronted him. "Right, Arthur, you had better not say anything to them. On the letter, it said only for a short time, for a special project, so this may not be a long-term job and I want to go and do it, so please don't spoil it for me. They are not happy with me as it is, and this will destroy any slight bit of a chance that I have at going. Promise me you won't say anything." She pleaded. "Alright." Arthur replied, "I won't say anything as long as you promise to be my girl and come walking with me every day until you leave to go to London and then, be my girl when you come home from London." Rose didn't feel she had much choice, she was thinking it's only for a walk, it can't do any harm, so she agreed.

For the next two weeks, Arthur would call on Rose and they would go for their walks, sometimes, Rose would bring Jim along for the walk, although Arthur was not keen when

Jim came. Arthur would always try and find excuses as to why Jim should not come on the walk. Excuses like; it was too cold, too wet or Jim looked too tired. Rose would not listen to the excuses and if Jim wanted to join them for their walks, then he could. Rose's parents, Elizabeth and James liked Arthur, and thought it would be a good idea if he and Rose became serious enough to marry one day. She spoke to Rose to tell her of their approval of Arthur and that the two of them should marry. Elizabeth looked to use the connection between Arthur and Rose as a way to get Rose to change her mind about going to London and make Arthur and Jim her priority. Rose couldn't believe what she was hearing from her own mother but thought she could come to some agreement which would allow her to go to London. She told her mother that if they let her go to London for the few weeks to do this job, and if they looked after Jim whilst she was away, that she would consider thinking about Arthur when she came back. Elizabeth and James thought about Rose's proposal, and the next day, they gave Rose their blessing, with the conditions that she had to go out with Arthur on her return.

# Chapter 9

# FEELS LIKE HOME

The day came for Rose to leave for London. Although Rose was excited, she felt calm and composed compared to the last trip. Her father took her to the station, Rose had a suitcase with her for this trip, it was small but enough for what she needed to take. The train journey from Hereford to London was quiet. Rose sat there admiring the landscape but not reacting the way she did previously. This was her way of feeling empowered by her choices and that she had already succeeded. Rose arrived in London and got off the train and knew exactly where she needed to go to get a taxi. Counting every single step until she got into the next available taxi. She instructed the driver where she was heading, and the taxi began its journey through the streets of London. Passing the streets of people, Rose felt that she belonged here in the city. As the time passed, the taxi driver told her that they were approaching Buckingham Palace. Rose exited and paid the fare and said to the taxi driver, "I could get used to this." The driver replied, "If you pass it every day, you do get used to it. Enjoy your visit, Miss." Rose concluded, "I'm not visiting, I work here."

Rose waited for the taxi to leave, before reaching into her handbag to pull out the letter that instructed her where she needed to go to on her first day. Rose approached the gate, fighting her overpowering feelings of anxiety and nervousness, with the biggest breath she could inhale, she exhaled and lifted her head and walked to the side entrance. Hughes met Rose at the door. "Come on in Davies." Hughes told Rose, as if she was opening her own front door to her. Rose walked down the corridor, and with each step further into the building, Rose began becoming more optimistic with her confidence. "Where do I have to go?" Rose asked. "I don't think you are staying here at the moment as they are having renovations in the servants quarters. I'm not sure what is happening but you and me are having to go to York House for a while. To the servant's quarters there. It's small and pokey." Hughes said. Rose looked confused. Hughes continued that, "they don't have many servants and staff there. It's where the Prince of Wales lives." Rose's eyes opened with excitement, "What's he like?" she asked. "I have never met him personally. They say he is ignorant and rude to his staff if things are not done to his liking. Other staff have said that he is a very nice young man and treats them well. Do not worry about it either way, I doubt we will ever see him." Hughes remarked, "Will I have a room of my own?" Rose enquired. Hughes chuckled, "A room of your own. Do you think you'll be having afternoon tea with the family? Let me tell you something, you will be expected to do as you are told. Just remember, you haven't got the job yet. They don't get you to come here twice and not give you the job but just remember, we are here to work." Hughes grabbed her case and off she left with Rose. "Where will we get a taxi?" Rose asked. "We are not getting a taxi. We have to walk. The other staff got a lift in one of the cars but there was no room for us so we will have to walk." Hughes said. She pointed at Rose's legs and joked, "There you go girl, your very own built-in taxi. Start your motor and off we go." The two of them could not stop giggling to one another as they headed down the road from the palace. When they were further away from the Palace, Rose hailed a taxi and told Hughes to get in. Hughes was unsure what to say or do but Rose told her she will pay for the fare, as she had some money left from the train fare. Rose told the driver to head to York House, and they headed off but not before Rose told Hughes that her legs that she claimed were her taxi, are needing repairs as they were too tired before they both erupted with laughter.

They pulled up as close to York House as they could and were greeted at the staff entrance by a Housemaid named Page. Hughes told Page they were from the Palace, and Page, looking baffled, told Hughes and Rose that they weren't expecting them and that the rest of the staff have already arrived. We weren't expecting you for another half an hour." "We came by taxi." Hughes replied. "Davies paid for it. She is from the country; they are different to us, but it was great fun. I have never been in a taxi before." Hughes confessed. Williams, the Butler, came down to the servants' hall. "Right, you lot." He addressed, "You will be joining us for a few weeks until the work at the Palace is done. The roof is leaking, and you lot have a bad case of rats, so you have had to come and join us here. You have to share rooms but Mrs Gray, the head Housekeeper, will tell you all about that as it's now time for tea. You must all head to the dining room where you will be told what is happening."

There were a few people in the dining room; several footmen, the butler, Mrs Gray, an older woman with the grumpiest face you could ever imagine, Francis Gray, who was younger and a Maid, Smith, who was another Maid, and Page, who had greeted Rose and Hughes at the door. Rose was quizzed by several members of staff and had to explain the same to each of them that she is a seamstress. Page tried to mock Rose by exploiting to the other members of staff that she had got a taxi here with Hughes and that she had paid for it herself. Rose felt cornered and felt she had to defend herself by explaining that her legs were tired, that she had some spare money from her train fare and that she had been travelling most of the day to get there.

Mrs Gray dismissed them all and sent them to their rooms before imposing the rules.

"The rules of this house. You do not speak to any member of the family unless you are spoken to first. You do not offer them any assistance with anything. You come and find me or Mr Williams. If there is a guest who needs anything, you listen to their request and then, again, you come and tell either myself or Mr Williams. Is that understood? You do not look the family in the eye, you keep your head bowed at all times when they are in the room. If they do get your attention, you curtsey and then move on as quickly as possible. Do not linger. Now, you can go." As the staff were beginning to leave, Smith muttered "Come on, move before she finds something else to say. I will show you to your room. You are staying one floor up from the Prince of Wales. Don't get your hopes up of seeing him, he's out most of the time but watch out for his private secretary. He's a right misery." "Have you ever seen the Prince?" Rose asked. Smith quietly replied, "I have but you need to watch him. He has made advances after several staff here and they have all ended up leaving. You are all right at the moment, rumour has it, he has another woman in tow. It's only when he gets an urge he goes after the staff." Rose and Hughes went to their room. Rose could not stop thinking about the Prince of Wales below her. Not once did Arthur or Jim pass her thoughts.

# Chapter 10

## STAY IN HER GOOD BOOKS

The next day, Rose and Hughes were shown to the room where the sewing needed mending. The uniform Rose was given looked loose and baggy. She could not carry on with the day wearing it and took a needle and thread and slipped down the top of the dress. "It's supposed to be like that. Rose what are you doing? Someone might come in and see you," Hughes panicked. Rose quickly sewed the bust on her uniform dress. "There we go," Rose gloated. "Would you like me to fix yours?" "No, I don't," Hughes replied, "Mine has looked like this since I started." There was a pile of sewing to do, curtains needed mending where they had come unstitched and frayed on the edges. "We should do this on the treadle machine," Rose remarked. "I know, but the machine is at the Palace. I think it's all hand-sewing down here," Hughes responded. They both picked up a curtain each. Rose began watching Hughes and suggested, "If you over sew where it's frayed, it will hold it in place for longer." Although Hughes was good at sewing, she had never seen sewing in that way and copied Rose's actions. They sewed for hours, and Mrs Gray came in to look at their work. "Right girls, it's time for a cuppa. Go to the kitchen and have a break," She ordered. Hughes told Rose that if Mrs Gray is telling us to go for a break, that they were doing really good work.

Rose and Hughes were sat in the kitchen drinking tea, watching staff members enter and leave non-stop. They all wore different uniforms, so much so that you could not guess what the next uniform to come into the kitchen would be. Rose asked Hughes what each uniform was for, and Hughes explained each one as quickly as she could as they were there and gone within a few moments. The time passed quickly, and it was time for them to return to the sewing room and continue their work.

"When we finish work and go back to the room, I will take a needle and some thread and take in this dress at the waist, so it will fit me properly. It's like wearing a sack" Moaned Rose. "It's not that bad" Hughes quipped. "No one is going to see you anyway; we all look the same." Rose rebelled, "I know but I want to look different." With an unimpressed look, Hughes warned Rose, "Be careful Davies, different in a place like this might not go down too well." After they finished their sewing, they went to their room.

"Do you have any family?" Hughes asked. Rose was struck by that question as that was the first time that her family had entered her thoughts. Hesitantly, Rose disclosed, "Yes, I have a sister and my parents, they run a farm in Hereford." There was no mention of her son, Jim, nothing about her being married before, or that she was a widow. Rose quickly took control of the conversation before she was asked more questions. "Do you have a family?" Hughes sat up, "I have two brothers and three sisters. My brothers and two sisters are in service like me, but the youngest is too young at the moment and is still at home. My mother and father, I see them once a year, if I am lucky, otherwise we write once a month. Are you going to send any letters home Rose?" "I am only here for a short while so I don't think I will bother" Rose replied. Hughes pointed out to Rose, "I was only supposed to be here for six to eight weeks. That was four years ago." Rose took off her dress and began working on it, she took it in around the waist so it would fit her better. "Don't cut anything off it Rose" Hughes warned. "I expect you will have to let it out again when Gray sees it. Like I said, she doesn't do different." Rose altered the dress and put it back on. "Right, it's time for tea I think" Hughes urged.

In the kitchen, they sat at the table and waited for everyone to arrive. Their tea was soup, bread, and a wedge of fruitcake for pudding. The staff chatted amongst themselves. They asked Rose where she was from and why she wanted a job at York House. "I didn't want to come here" Rose expressed. "I am supposed to be living at the Palace, not here." Williams looked at Rose with a disgusted look, "This place not good enough for you then?" He smirked which broke the worry of hostility. "It's not that. It's the fact that I am not supposed to be here. The interview and position is to be there," Rose explained. Rose then stood up and everyone could see what she had done to her dress. It fitted her like a glove, showing her bust and waist. Smith gasped, "Oh my, what have you done to that, and can you fix mine?" Then a voice entering the room pierced the moment, "No she most certainly cannot." It was Mrs Gray the Housekeeper, she continued, "and when she goes back to her room, she can alter it back to how it was. It's not a fashion parade, you are no different to the rest of the maids." she growled. All eyes were on Rose and Mrs Gray when Rose countered, "I am not a maid, I am a seamstress and think my clothes should at least fit me properly." Before anyone could pick their jaw off the floor, Mrs Gray stood toe to toe with Rose and asserted herself, "Well, I am in charge here and I am telling you. Not asking you, Miss taxi rider, who seems to think she is better than everyone else. Change your uniform back to how it was." Rose left the kitchen and Hughes quickly followed, nagging, "I told you Rose, I told you, she can be such a cow, she is like it to everyone, don't be upset." Rose huffed, "I am not upset, and I am not going to change my dress to how it was, she can please herself."

The next morning, everyone met for breakfast and Rose was still in the fitted dress and everybody tried to lower their heads, waiting for Mrs Gray to explode, but before she could say anything, Rose apologised, "I am ever so sorry Mrs Gray, I didn't realise I could not alter this dress so it would fit more properly, I cannot change it back as I had already cut off the extra fabric and now there is nothing to alter, but I am ever so sorry. If you can give me another dress, I will of course not alter it and promise to wear it as it is." Mrs Gray took a breath and accepted Rose's apology and said she should wear her dress and that she shouldn't alter anything else without permission. Rose went to the sewing room, Hughes and Lewis were already there. "Well, what did the old bag say this time? How come you are in the same dress?" they both asked. "I apologised and I kept apologising until she accepted it thinking I meant it and it worked," Rose bubbled. "Well, I never, she has never let anyone get away with anything, ever. Has she Hughes?" Lewis marvelled. Rose looked at them and they all began laughing with curiosity as to how Rose could change the way Mrs Gray was. "Well, I am different" Rose cackled.

Rose got on well with Hughes and Lewis, they explained why they took a position at the palace, where it took them away from their families. Lewis started talking, "we all lived in one house, my mother, father, gran, my dad's brother, who was blind. Then there was also my sister and my twin sisters. All of us in a three-bedroom house. It was all right, a bit tight to say the least but we managed. My dad worked making barrels for the local brewery, so my mother had one wage coming in. We had to grow everything we could in the smallest patch of garden which was shared with the neighbours. One of the neighbours had chickens, and the old boy further on down, had a goat. Bloody stunk it did. It did not give any milk on account it was male. No one knew why he kept it, but he liked it. Any scraps from the garden were given to him. He was always very glad and in return, he would do a lot of weeding in the garden. It was a nice place to live, mum and dad slept in the parlour, Uncle Dick slept in the small room at the top of the stairs. Gran, me, and my sister slept in the big room and the big cupboard at the end of the passage, which mother insisted on calling the third bedroom, that the twins were in. Nothing else only a bed that dad had made to fit the whole cupboard. Sorry, I meant third bedroom. So as soon as I was old enough, I had to leave and find somewhere I would be looked after. I could not find a job anywhere near home, so I left and came down here. I asked at the door when someone was going into the Palace if there was anything going, and I came in as a scullery maid. I was ever so pleased. I had a job straight away. Clothes to wear and a bed and I was on my own in the room for nearly a year before Smith joined me. I had never had a bed on my own, I could not sleep for weeks. I missed sharing that big bed with my gran and my sister. Funny isn't it, but that's how it was. I go home to see them twice a year. Nothing has changed there. I mean, gran looks like death has come for her twice, but she has insisted she's not ready. Uncle Dick still cannot see a bloody thing, not that I thought his sight would ever improve, but gran thought it might come back one day, and the girls are growing. Mum was hoping gran would hurry up and die so the twins could move out of the cupboard and into the bigger bedroom with my sister. That's my life".

Rose and Hughes looked at one another and Rose hinted to Hughes to tell her story. "Well," Said Hughes, "I have two older brothers who work for the Earl of Morley, they are well looked after and enjoy their work, although they say it is long and tiring. I have not seen either of them for years, but they write home two or three times a month; one letter between the two and sometimes when they are given extra by the Earl, they will send a bit home. My sisters work at the big house down the road from where we used to live. They are allowed to go home every day, so they see our parents all the time. I couldn't get anything near home. My dad heard this was a good place to work so he sent a letter in and here I am." Hughes looked at Rose and Lewis before continuing, "I would have come here to do anything mind, cooks' assistant because I can cook, household staff 'cause I can clean to a high standard, well I think I can, and like the two of you, I can sew and the vacancy was available, so I got the job to help with the sewing. What about you Rose?" Rose looked a bit uncertain of what to say as Hughes and Lewis were open and honest. She began confiding in her two new friends. "Well, as you know, I am from Hereford, completely different to London.

In Hereford, everybody knows everybody. I helped out with my sister on my parents' farm. Dad took on other work for other farmers, and my sister May helped him with that, more than I did. I tried to help mum as much as I could, but I always felt I could do more. I saw one of the local lads in the market and he told me he was working for King George, and that's what made me write to the Palace and ask if there was any work". Lewis chimed in, "What did he do, the boy you just mentioned?" Rose looked at Lewis thinking she may know Arthur and disclosed, "Oh Arthur, he picked up birds when he was working on the shoots and met the King four or five times. The way he told it; it was as though he knew the King personally. You should see him, he's short and scruffy. He's usually quite shy but when he starts, there's no way to shut him up". Lewis and Hughes were fascinated by Rose's story, "What did he think when you got the job here?" Hughes asked. Rose continued telling her story, "He was surprised and told me that people in London were strange, and I should watch myself. Some of the stories he told me would melt my ears, they were that bad. He had heard the gossip from the maids and a couple of Footmen, but I have no idea what he thought he knew." Rose concluded her story and the three of them carried on with the curtains. Hughes could see that there may be more that Rose was hiding but mentioned, "These were supposed to be hung back up yesterday, so we had better get on with it. Otherwise, Mrs Gray will wonder what's going on". They concentrated on their sewing and within a few hours, the curtains were finally finished.

# Chapter 11

# A JOB WELL DONE

L ewis informed Mrs Gray of the work they had completed, and Mrs Gray passed on the information to Mr Williams. Two of the male house-staff were called to carry the curtains to the room in which they were to be rehung. Mrs Gray called Rose, Lewis, and Hughes to her room. The three of them thought they may have done something wrong with the curtains or that they were going to be in trouble for taking too long fixing them. When they entered the room, Mrs Gray turned to them and nodded, "There is an important sewing task that will need to be completed within the next three months. A dress has arrived for Her Majesty, and she wants an applique on it. You three will have to hand-sew every detail to the very best standard." Mrs Gray's head turned sharply to Rose, "Rose, I know you have done this before so you will sew the main bodice, shoulders and neckline, keeping the stitches as fine as you can." Her head then swiped to Lewis and Hughes. "Lewis, Hughes. You will help Rose with the rest of it and down the skirt to the hemline. Everything that is needed to complete this will arrive tomorrow by ten o'clock, no later. Make sure it is started on time. Any questions?" The three of them shook their heads. Mrs Gray pointed out, "Good, oh, and by the way, the work is to be done at the Palace so it's an early start. I have arranged for a car to pick you up, so no taxis Davies. Off you go, no time to waste."

Rose, Hughes, and Lewis shrunk in relaxation and looked at each other, excited at the prospect of sewing Her Majesty's dress. Rose could not contain her excitement and bubbled to Hughes and Lewis, "Do you think we will see her in it? You know, for the fitting?" Lewis knocked down the dream. "I doubt it. She has a dresser who does that kind of thing". Rose was more interested in going to the Palace than sewing the dress. Rose gushed, "I want to see the King. I want to say hello. Arthur has done it and I want to do it too." Lewis interjected, "You cannot speak to the King. Not at all, he doesn't speak to the likes of us." Rose was upset by the thought of not being able to speak to the King. "Well, Arthur reckons he spoke to him several times." She whined. Lewis and Hughes looked at Rose and Lewis clarified, "Look Rose, we are not allowed to speak to any of the family until we are spoken to. That is the rule. Remember that Rose or we will all be in trouble." Hughes could see Rose was about to whinge more about the matter. "Rose, just shut up about Arthur. He's not here and I thought you didn't like him anyway; you always moan about him." Rose didn't mention Arthur again and they carried on with the work they had to complete that day.

Monday morning at 6am and the sun was trying to break through the clouds. Rose, Hughes, and Lewis were up and ready to leave York House for their short journey to Buckingham Palace. Lewis was talking to a delivery boy about the van he had that morning. "Any chance you would take the three of us to the Palace as we are working there this week." The delivery boy looked at the three of them and replied, "I have only got one seat in the front next to me, but if the other two don't mind riding in the back, then I will take you, but you've got to get a move on as I can't be late with my deliveries." The three ladies grabbed their things and hurried to the van. Lewis sat in the front, while Hughes and Rose had to climb in the back of the van, squeezing in with all the overhanging crates of vegetables, which felt like they were growing more and more every minute. The delivery boy shut the doors, he jumped in the front with Lewis and began driving. The smell was very strong, and Hughes joked, "I hope the doors don't fly open and the veg falls out. Or worse, we fall out with it." Rose was trying to hold her breath to help combat the smell of cabbages. Hughes and Rose could hear mumbling in the front between Lewis and the delivery boy and then suddenly, the van came to a halt and veg began falling on top of Hughes and Rose. The delivery boy opened the backdoor of the van and helped Rose and Hughes out. Rose gasped for air, "I hope this bloody smell doesn't linger." Lewis thanked the delivery boy for the lift. He gave Lewis a smile and a wave as he climbed back into the van and drove off along the Mall away from the Palace. Lewis began telling Rose and Hughes the delivery boy's name and that he asked if Lewis would like to go for a walk with him, or they could arrange to go to the cinema together. Rose was still uncertain if the smell of the vegetables were staining her clothes and hair not paying attention to Lewis, but Hughes chirped in, "He's a fast worker isn't he. You only met him twenty minutes ago." An eruption of laughter followed. They were met by a footman who told them to shut up and be quiet. They were shown into the Palace and towards the sewing room. "I know where it is, I've worked here long enough, I certainly don't need you to show me the way," Hughes boasted. The footman confronted Hughes, "Well if you work here, why have you come from somewhere else then?" Just as Hughes was going to give the footman an earful, they were at the sewing room.

Rose rushed over to the treadle machine; it filled her with excitement. Admiring the machine, Rose confessed, "If I didn't get this job, I was going to get myself one of these." Hughes looked at Rose rubbing her hand across every inch of the machine. "I remember you saying that the first time you came here, I didn't think you were serious though. It would be the last thing I would buy if I could buy myself something." Just as Rose was about to respond, the door opened, and all three stood on their feet to attention as the dress was brought in. It came in a very large travelling box, sealed with a satin ribbon. The box was opened in front of them, revealing the most beautiful dress, although it was plain to look at, the ladies were in awe of its beauty. The high neck, the leg of mutton sleeves and the fabric itself, was of the finest quality. Rose, Hughes, and Lewis had never seen anything quite like it ever before. Mrs Gray entered the room carrying different fabrics and the three ladies knew that they were going to have to listen carefully to her instructions. "Right girls, this is for the applique, cut carefully. The pattern of which Her Majesty has chosen is already on the cutting table. Rose, the colours are written down. Do not, under any circumstances, change the order of colour, as each leaf and flower represent something. Let me know of any problems, Anything at all." The three ladies looked at the fabrics, cottons, and the pattern. The reality of the importance of their task hit them all. "I've never done anything like this before," Rose wavered, looking at Lewis and Hughes, "Have you?" Lewis and Hughes began shaking their heads, "No, nothing like this. I heard there was a woman named Handley, who sews this kind of thing. Why isn't she doing it?" Hughes asked. Lewis took control, "Right, ours is not to reason why." As she passed the scissors to Rose, "You heard Mrs Gray, Rose, cut bloody carefully as we don't have spare fabric for any mistakes." Rose looked at the pattern carefully absorbing every bit of information and detail. "There's something wrong with the way this is drawn!" Rose yelped. "Look. When you have the fabric overlap, it will be too thick and won't hold right on the dress. I need to speak to Mrs Gray."

Rose began pacing around the Palace, asking every footman as she passed by if they had seen Mrs Gray. She was told several times that she should not be in those parts of the Palace and to go back to her room. Rose began ignoring the orders she was given and was admiring each painting in every room, on every staircase and down every corridor. All shapes and sizes, some paintings bigger than her and almost as tall as the room itself. She began looking at the floor placing one foot behind the other, carefully walking through the main corridor which seemed to go on for miles. Rose began wondering who the people were in each painting, reacting to each one with a different thought; How some of them were ugly, why they would be on show for everyone to see, towering the guests and staff.

Rose continued searching for Mrs Gray and came across an upstairs maid. "Have you seen Mrs Gray?" Rose asked. "It is very important that I find her." The maid hastily approached Rose, "What are you doing up here? Mrs Gray will have your guts for garters. You're not allowed up here, leave now! Use the servants' stairs. Hurry, follow me, I'll lead you to the stairs, before you are seen by the family or guests." Rose was too naive to understand what the fuss was about. She hurried down the stairs to the kitchen and found Mrs Gray. "Mrs Gray, I have been searching for you all around the Palace." Mrs Gray jumped to her feet. "What? All over the Palace?" She screeched. The staff in the kitchen continued working but listened in to the conversation. Rose realised that she may have been in the wrong. "I can't start the sewing without speaking to you. It's urgent." Realising Rose was serious about the urgency, Mrs Gray stiffened her posture and calmly told Rose that she would help, looking at the kitchen staff sternly which made them hurry their work.

Rose showed Mrs Gray the drawn pattern. Rose began explaining, "It won't work if I do it like this." Mrs Gray couldn't see the error in the pattern, "Why? It looks alright to me." She queried. Rose continued explaining, "It's the weight of the fabric, so many pieces on top of one another. It won't hang properly! And, seeing as it is around her neck, it won't be very comfortable." Mrs Gray still looked puzzled. Rose concluded, "Here, let me show you." Rose took several pieces of fabric and placed them how it would have been if sewn onto the dress. Mrs Gray began to realise that Rose was right and that it wouldn't work doing it the way it is drawn. Mrs Gray took control of the room, "Right! I will have to ask permission for the pattern to be changed, and while I am away, stay out of trouble and out of the way of the other staff. They all have work to do you know. You can sew the other curtain, no time to waste."

The curtains were old and practically thread bare. Rose never lived in a palace before but was repelled by the state of the curtains. "Would you hang these in your house?" Hughes shook her head as Lewis stated, "They need a bloody good wash." The ladies began smiling at Lewis' comment before Rose quipped, "They need the bin more than a wash." The three of them began chuckling, "I bet these are from the servants' quarters. No wonder they have rats in the belfry if the curtains are this bad" Lewis said. Hughes interrupted, "Don't you mean bats, bats in the belfry, not rats." Rose shrieked, "They have bats here? I am not sleeping anywhere that have bats flying around, lurking in the dark." Mrs Gray entered the room, "What is this noise about girls?" She inquired. Lewis and Hughes stepped back before Rose confronted Mrs Gray, "Well, you have bats and rats, and god knows what else here and, if we have to come back here to stay, I'm sorry, I can't stay in a place where there's bats and rats, Palace or not." Mrs Gray looked bemused, "What nonsense. Who told you that there are bats and rats?" Hughes stepped up front, "It was me miss. I was trying to tell Rose that there are bats in the belfry, not rats." Mrs Gray rasped, "Well, we now have neither rat, nor bat, only a leaky roof which should be fixed shortly and then you can all come back to stay here. Does that suit your personal requirements Davies? I have told the dressmaker about your observation regarding the dress and fabric. The reply is what they have explained in the first place, so get on with it." Rose was not impressed as she knew they had not given those instructions for sewing the dress, and if Rose had not figured it out in the first instance, it would have been a huge mistake. Rose was unimpressed that her concern had been claimed by someone else as their own. Mrs Gray could see the frustration in Rose's eyes, "I know Rose. Believe me, I know but sometimes ours is not to reason why. I'm sorry Rose."

Rose bit her tongue and continued with the work of cutting out the intricate flowers and leaves ready for sewing. It took careful precision to cut around both flowers and leaves, Hughes and Lewis were waiting silently for Rose to finish so they could continue with the sewing. They could see Rose was upset so decided to continue mending the smelly tatty curtains.

# Chapter 12

# THE PRINCE AND THE SEAMSTRESS

It was time for them to leave the Palace and head back to York House. They left the Palace gates and began looking for a car to take them, but Rose said that she felt like walking back. Hughes and Lewis grabbed Rose around the shoulder, comforting her. "We'll walk with you, then you can tell us about what you saw around the palace and if you saw any cute men for Lewis." Hughes joked. Lewis tried not to smile at that comment and Rose beamed, "Well, there weren't any cute men there, but I can tell you about the carpets, curtains, and how awful some of the paintings were. Oh, and the rooms, the beds, the covers, and the furniture. It was all beautiful." They continued walking back towards York House and Lewis asked if Hughes and Rose wanted to go to the cinema with her, and the delivery boy the next day. "I think this could be something serious," Lewis told Hughes and Rose. "Can either of you remember what he said his name is?" Hughes and Rose looked at each other and laughed, "Something serious?" Rose chuckled, "His name is Fred." Hughes looked at Rose and chirped, "Oh, Lewis, I think you may have competition, I think Rose likes Fred too." Rose was taken aback by Hughes's comment, "No, not at all, I knew a Fred once. He was tall and dark, he had muscles, no manners to speak of but when he put his arms around me, I knew he was there, you know, a good strong squeeze." Lewis and Hughes stopped walking and Lewis turned to Rose, "Woah, tell us more, Rose. How long did you know him? Was it serious?" Rose was uncertain what to say but knew she liked being around Hughes and Lewis and responded, "Yes, It was serious." She continued her story and reached the part of Fred drowning when Hughes spluttered with tears, "Oh Rose, that's terrible." Lewis was emotionally tougher than Hughes and Rose, she tried to lighten the mood and with a grin, blurted, "Well I hope my Fred doesn't drown." Hughes gasped at the comment Lewis made as Rose tried to crack a smile. Rose knew Lewis meant well but at the same time had a mouth that she couldn't control.

They made it back to York House in time for tea. After they finished, Rose stood and announced that she was going to go to bed early as she was feeling tired from the cutting out of the leaves and flowers. She left the table and began heading upstairs, but instead of going to the servants' quarters, she snuck through the door that led her to the main part of the house. She could not hear any noise and thought she was alone. They were not told of any family in the house or other staff, and she was curious about what it looked like in that part of the house. She slowly walked along each corridor, looking at everything. All the ornaments, pictures, curtains, and carpets, comparing them to what she saw earlier that day in the Palace. She continued admiring what she saw until her eye caught sight of a figure in the corner of her eye. Rose froze where she stood and then slowly, without turning around, put one foot behind the other and started walking backwards as the figure in the corner began following her footsteps. A voice bounced off each corner of the corridor, "May I help you?" Rose stopped and the figure of a skinny, shorter man with fair hair, appeared. Rose quickly bowed her head, not to look him in the eye. She quivered, "Sorry sir, I was just looking at the hallway and paintings. I didn't touch anything." She began heading back to the door she entered through. "Who are you and what are you doing here?" the voice demanded. "My name is Rose, sir," Rose whispered. "Are you a new maid or something?" Rose's knees began shaking, "No sir, I'm the new seamstress, sir. I'm supposed to be at the Palace, but they have rats and bats or bats and cats, in the belfry, so I have had to come here." a chuckle from the man brightened the room, "Rats and bats. Do we have a belfry Rose?" Rose lifted her eyes just to see the smile from the voice she had been responding to. "That's what I was told, sir. That's why we are here to stay for a little while. Though Mrs Gray said we will be going back to the Palace soon. Is there anything you need sir?" The man shook his head. "You are the prince, aren't you? The Prince of Wales? The man's voice became clearer and more assertive. "That's right Rose, I am. Where are you heading now?" Rose's eyes widened with shock that she was talking to the Prince of Wales. "I have to go back to my room, sir. I shouldn't be here." The prince began speaking to Rose with power and demand in his voice, "Well Rose, One is bored and finds the need to talk to someone. Would you like to talk with me Rose?" Rose became tongue tied and with a croak in her voice, mumbled, "We are not allowed to speak to the Royal Family sir, or any of the guests. That's one of the rules we were told on our first day." The prince could see Rose was unsure of herself and he leaned towards her, "Bugger the rules Rose, come and talk to me." With the voice blowing into her ears, Rose and the prince walked into his room and the door closed gently behind.

Rose became more and more relaxed, the further she moved into the room. She was admiring the craftsmanship in the furniture and paintings on the wall when the prince began asking, "so Rose, tell me about yourself." Rose told the prince about what she called the most boring life. "Nothing much has ever happened in my life, except…." The prince was intrigued, "Except what?" Rose was about to tell him about being a widow but overcame that urge and quickly responded, "Well, I met Arthur Powell and he told me he had not only met the king, but he had also spoken to him at least four times on four different occasions." The prince got closer to Rose, "Well, the next time you see Arthur Powell, you can tell him you spoken to the Prince of Wales." Rose blushed with embarrassment. Not only was she breaking the rules, but she was looking the prince in the eye and sitting in his personal room. Thoughts were rushing through her head, and she leapt up. "I had better go now sir or the others will wonder where I have gone." The prince stood to lead Rose towards the door, thanking her for her time and the talk, as Rose quietly crept out of the room the door closing tightly behind her.

**Edward VIII**
(This photograph was given by Mr Wigram to my father)

## Chapter 13

# WHERE HAVE YOU BEEN?

Rose rushed back to her room with Hughes and Lewis waiting for her to return. "Where have you been Rose? We were getting worried, it's been over half an hour, where did you go?" Hughes questioned. Rose knew she could not tell the truth to them as Lewis would likely not keep the secret and everyone would find out; So, Rose told them she had been sitting outside getting some fresh air as she was missing the countryside. Hughes was not fooled by the lie, but Lewis believed her and told her that the countryside will still be there when she goes home. It was soon time for their evening tea, and they had to get ready to go to the kitchen, when Rose began to sit down on her bed. "I'm not feeling hungry tonight. I think I will give tea a miss." Hughes was concerned for Rose, "Are you not feeling well? Would you like me to bring you something from the kitchen?" Rose told Hughes that she was feeling fine, she was just not hungry. Lewis and Hughes left to go to the kitchen, Rose was laying on her bed reflecting on what had happened and pinching herself to make sure she was not dreaming. I met the prince. The prince met me. He asked me to chat to him. The Prince of Wales. As time passed, Hughes came into the room and sat on the edge of Rose's bed, "Alright Rose, what have you done? I could tell by the look on your face you have done something. Now, come on, let's have it." Rose sat herself upright and leant into Hughes, "Right, but you have to promise that you won't tell anyone, and I mean, really promise." Hughes was more eager to hear what Rose had to say and promised not to tell a soul. "I spoke to the Prince of Wales, and he asked me to chat to him in his room." Hughes could tell that Rose was telling the truth, "Oh my goodness, what did he say to you," Hughes asked. Rose told Hughes everything about how his voice was dominating and echoed along the corridor and at the end asked Hughes not to tell anyone, not even Lewis as she would be in the kitchen telling everyone that went in there. Hughes promised again not to tell and warned Rose that she would be in big trouble if the prince mentioned anything.

Lewis came into the room boasting about how much food there was down there and how she had thirds. "I am going to the cinema with Fred tomorrow. Would either of you like to come?" She asked. Hughes said she would go as she had not been to the cinema for a long time, but Rose kindly declined the offer. Hughes told Lewis it was probably as Rose was not feeling well, both Rose and Hughes knew it was something else.

The next evening, Hughes and Lewis had left for the cinema. Rose began stalking the corridors in York House praying for the chance of bumping into the Prince of Wales. She waited for the footman to go on his break and stood in the doorway trying to give away the sense of her presence. Almost ten minutes went by and then, there he was. The prince had come home. He saw Rose there and smiled, tilting his head down slightly to acknowledge her presence. Rose bowed her head to the prince in response but quickly looked away as his Private Secretary was with him, and he almost caught Rose staring at the prince. Rose slowly closed the door but kept listening, waiting for the voices to stop. She could not tell if the voices had stopped or not as it became too quiet and decided to open the door, just enough to peak through. She could see the prince talking to one of his members of staff.

He caught a glimpse of Rose peeking through, and as the member of staff left, he waved to Rose, and she burst through the door and quickly walked to the prince's room. The door was open waiting for her to enter. "Come in wosey posey. How are you this evening?" Rose was hit by the pet-name the prince had just given her. "I'm fine, sir and how are you?" The prince began opening up to Rose. "It's been a hell of a day Rose. Boring meetings with boring people. But enough of my boring day. Tell me about yours." Rose sat down as if she was talking to Hughes and began unloading every word she had about her day to the Prince of Wales. How she worked at the Palace and how she was sewing the Queen's dress with the extra bits of fabric. She could tell the prince did not know much about what she was saying so began explaining what an applique was. He seemed extremely interested in what Rose had to say, "tell me about you Rose. Tell me about your life." She told him about her life on the farm and how and why she wanted to come to London. The prince stopped Rose continuing, "If you could have anything in the world right now Rose, what would it be?" Rose began thinking of the most bizarre thing she could at that moment. "Well, if I could have anything right now, it would be a full-length fur coat." The prince laughed at Rose's decision. "That's right, a fur coat. When I came for my interview here in London, I saw a lady wear one and it was the most beautiful full-length fur coat I had ever seen. What about you sir. What would you have if you could choose anything?" The Prince of Wales reacted as if he had never been asked that question before. "Right now, Rose? I don't have the answer." Rose thought he was just boasting about having everything as he is the Prince of Wales. "Well, I suppose you being a prince, sir, you have everything and anything you want." The prince looked at Rose and sighed, "If only you knew the half of it." Rose did not understand what he meant by that comment but carried on the conversation about the fur coat she could only dream of.

"I have to go away for a few days. I will be back on Thursday. Would you like to see me again Rose? Maybe have a cup of tea or something?" Rose beamed and could not believe that she was speaking to the Prince of Wales as if they had been friends for years. "You had better go now Rose." She stood up and curtsied low to the ground. "Thank you, sir."

"I would very much like to see you Thursday." she stated. "What if your staff see me coming and going?" Rose asked. "Do not worry about them. I shall make sure they are not here. Goodnight Rose." Rose left the room and began slowly swaying as she walked back to her room, eagerly waiting for Hughes to return from the cinema, Rose was bursting to tell her about what had happened. Rose began warming to the reality that the Prince of Wales wanted to spend time with her.

It was around 9:30pm when Hughes finally walked through the door. Like a dog waiting by the door for their owner to come home, Rose jumped up with excitement, "Where have you been?" Hughes had just began taking her coat off and replied, "We went to the cinema and then we went for a drink. I think Fred was more interested in me than Lewis. He kept trying to touch me. He sat in-between Lewis and I at the cinema, and then put his arms on the back of both seats. I told him to get off and I moved into the empty seat next to me. After the movie, he asked if we wanted to go for a drink and that he would drop us back home. The three of us went to the pub. It was horrible. We had one drink and then he brought us back. I had to sit in the back of that bloody stinking old van of his." Rose looked puzzled, "Where's Lewis?" Hughes continued, "The last I saw of her was his arms all over her and his face stuck to hers like a child against the window of a sweet shop. It was disgusting. I asked if she was all right and if she wanted me to wait but she put her thumb up and brushed me away, so as far as I know, she is still in the van with Fred. Anyway, forget about that, how was your evening? You are looking better. Looks like you have had some strong medication." Hughes and Rose began laughing. Rose grabbed Hughes by the hands and sat her down on the end of her bed, "Well, I saw him again tonight and I went to his room. We talked for a little while and then he asked me if I would like to see him again on Thursday." Hughes was shocked by what Rose told her. "Oh, my goodness, Rose, you and the Prince of Wales, who'd have thought it." They both began giggling. "But watch yourself Rose. You've heard the stories about him, they may be true." Rose quickly let go of Hughes's hands, "Ah, but maybe they're not true and he likes me for me. I am a big girl, and I can take care of myself."

The next morning at breakfast, everyone was chatting as the post arrived. a letter came for Lewis. She was ever so excited as not many letters came for her. She was a bit hesitant as she was not sure if it was good news or bad news, or where it was from. Mr Williams told Lewis to open it so they could all find out together. Lewis opened the envelope and pulled out the folded paper. She began reading the letter to herself before Mrs Gray told her to let them know what it said. "I'm not quite sure. It's from my mother, telling me about the family, which is good, but then it says Mr Morgan from down the road has been nighteed." a voice yelled out, "He's been what? nighteed?" Lewis continued "Yes, nighteed. It says Mr Morgan has been nighteed for doing good work." Everyone in the room was puzzled by the letter Lewis was reading. Mr Williams looked at Mrs Gray. Mr Williams held out his hand and took the letter from Lewis, "give it here girl," he said, and began reading it aloud. It read that Mr Morgan from down the road had been nighteed. The staff erupted with laughter.

"It's nothing bad, he has been knighted it should read, by the King. He will be a Lord now Lewis, not a mister. That's what it means. He has gone up in the world." Lewis became more composed, "Wow, Mr Morgan a Lord. He makes writing paper and cards. Quite fancy they are and very costly, mum said it's more for his paper than a week's shopping."

Mrs Gray cut the conversation with a simple clap of her hands. "Right girls. How is the dress coming along?" Rose jumped in, "I'm still cutting out the leaves but there should be some for Hughes and Lewis to start applying them to the dress this afternoon." Mrs Gray could tell that Rose was a bit chirpier than usual. "You are very bubbly today, Rose." Hughes and Rose quickly glanced at one another. "Yes, Mrs Gray. It's the excitement of sewing Her Majesty's dress. It's such an honour." Mrs Gray concluded, "Yes, indeed Rose, it is, so take care with it. I will be in soon but if you need anything, just wait in the room and I will be there shortly. No wandering. Right girls, no wandering."

# Chapter 14

## NEVER ASK A LADY HER AGE

Rose, Hughes, and Lewis were back in the room sewing the dress and were chatting to one another. "How old are you, Lewis?" Hughes asked. "I'm 22," she responded, but she looked much older. "Rose, what about you?" Rose was approaching 30 but didn't want to tell them so she got them to guess. Numbers were being thrown around like a dog kicking up leaves in the park. 21, 24, 25, 30, 47, 32. Rose had to stop them before they went any higher. "I'm 25. Well, nearly. I am 24 now but 25 soon." Hughes sputtered, "Ha, I was right, I guessed 24." Lewis corrected Hughes, "Yes but then you changed your mind, so you are not right." The two of them began bickering and Rose stepped in to stop it, "Does it really matter how old I am? It's really nothing to argue about, is it?" Hughes stepped down before Lewis boasted, "Did Hughes tell you about last night, Rose? How she was all over Fred? She wouldn't leave him alone." Hughes shook her head, "That's not true. He tried touching me and I was having none of it. He's a creep and you need to know that, watch yourself." Lewis became enraged, towering over Hughes, "The first lad that has taken an interest in me and you want him for yourself." Hughes continued to express her concerns about Fred's interests. Rose went back to work, cutting out the applique, she told the two of them to grow up, act their age, or their combined age, however old it may be.

Mrs Gray came into the room. The dress was on the mannequin. "Now girls, we need to keep a dustcover on this at all times. Not a single speck of anything is to land on this dress." Rose helped Mrs Gray blanket the dress with the cover, then she thanked Rose for her help and asked her, "what is with you today Rose?" Rose beamed, "Nothing." I'm feeling happy today. Just happy." It was soon lunch time, and they all made their way to the kitchen. The staff sitting at lunch noticed Rose was very quiet, everyone was asking if Rose was alright. Rose reassured them all, "I'm fine. I'm just thinking." Page interjected, "What about?" Rose reaffirmed, "Nothing really, different things going through my head." Mr Williams joined in with the questioning, "Are you missing home?" Rose said she was a little sad. She knew she had to say something to end the interrogation. She could not exactly tell them all about her feelings or thoughts about the Prince of Wales. Mrs Gray took Rose aside and told her that if she ever felt lonely, that she could always talk to her, and if Rose didn't have any stamps or paper, that she could use some of hers to write a letter home. Rose nodded and thanked Mrs Gray for her suggestion, but the only person Rose wanted to talk to was the prince. She gave Mrs Gray a smile and went back to the room to continue sewing. Lewis came in, "Right. I know something is going on. What is it?" Hughes tried to knock down any ideas that might have revealed Rose's secret. Lewis continued pressing for more information, "I'm not bloody stupid. I have seen how the pair of you are behaving. It's different to normal." Rose did not know what to say. She began panicking and Hughes could see that Rose felt cornered and may have exposed her secret that could have been bad for the two of them, so blurted, "Right, Lewis. You had better not tell anyone, but I want to try on that dress. I want to see what it feels like to be a queen, but Rose said it will not fit because I'm too fat, so I am going to lose weight and then try it on, but don't tell anyone or I will be in for it." Lewis sensed that it was a lie and responded, "You're lying. Rose is smiling and giggling all the time," Rose's eyes opened wide before she hesitated, "Do you not think it's funny? Every time you look at this dress and imagine Hughes trying to fit in it." Rose mimicked someone tightly squeezing into a dress as she continued, "The dress is at least two feet longer than Hughes and the waist is half the size of Hughes. She would look like two tyres have been tucked into the dress." Lewis erupted with laughter while looking at Hughes, "Well, I suppose it would be funny. I can't unsee that image now." Rose got Hughes's attention and mouthed, thank you.

The applique was applied to the neck of the dress and then starting down the one side of the bodice. They took a step back to look at the dress in awe, visualising how amazing it would look when it was finished, with the small stitches and detail in every thread. Mrs Gray entered the room and stood just in the doorway to get a full view of the dress on the mannequin and confessed, "That is going to be beautiful on her Majesty. I know she will be pleased with it when it is finished." Mrs Gray then turned on the spot and disappeared down the corridor.

Lewis looked at the clock and saw it was time for the three of them to head back to York House. "Would you like a ride with Fred this evening? He is coming to pick me up. Fred has said that he is going to make us official." Lewis was bubbling but Hughes and Rose were uncertain by Lewis' announcement. "How is he going to make it official?" Rose asked. "I don't know!" Lewis replied, "But that's what he told me. We are going to be official." Rose and Hughes declined the offer of a lift to York House. Hughes could not stand Fred after the way he had previously acted towards her and thought he was the wrong choice of man from the start. Rose declined as she was not in a rush to get to York House as the prince was not going to be there. Rose and Hughes gathered their bits and pieces and began walking down the Mall towards York House, taking their time to appreciate the views and the people passing them along the way.

# Chapter 15

# WHO DID THIS TO YOU?

When they arrived at York House, they were surprised not to see Lewis there waiting for them, so they decided to head inside and wait in the kitchen for her. They did not trust Fred and wanted to make sure she arrived safely back at York House. The clock was moving ever so slowly as the two of them waited for Lewis, it was getting later and later into the evening, the girls began to panic as they had let Lewis go off with Fred on her own. They saw Mrs Gray in the corner talking to someone, they approached her to tell her they were worried about Lewis. Mrs Gray told them she had no idea where Lewis could be and that she would tell Mr Williams. As Mrs Gray walked into the next room to inform Mr Williams, they heard the backdoor open, Rose looked into the hall to grab a glimpse of the figure who was entering. Completely erasing Lewis from her mind, she thought of how the figure reminded her of the prince but was then brought back to reality when Lewis stepped forward. She ran over to Rose with her arms open wide for a hug and tears streaming down her face. Mrs Gray came back in with Mr Williams, and she could see something wasn't right, asking the cook if she would make Lewis a cup of tea, as she sat Lewis down at the table. The cook noticed that Lewis couldn't find any words, as she kept choking on her tears, so cook added a little cooking brandy to the cup of tea. Mrs Gray pulled up a seat in front of Lewis and held her hand, comforting her, "My girl.

What has happened to you? Did that young man do this?" Rose brushed Lewis's hair back behind her shoulders, it was messed up as if she had been caught in a windstorm. Rose and Hughes gasped as they saw a mark on her neck. Mrs Gray was always protective of the ladies and held Lewis's hand firmly. Lewis began confiding with the staff in the room. "Fred said he would give me a lift and wanted to make our courting official. I had no idea what he meant by that, so I was surprised when he told me what he wanted me to do. It was more than kissing. He put his hands on me, in places where no gentleman should have them, well, not unless he is your husband." Some of the staff were shocked by the allegations and left the room in-disgust of what Lewis was saying. She continued telling her story. "He forced me backwards in that van of his. I raised my foot and pushed with all my might, he fell backwards against the steering wheel, and while he was caught up there, I lunged forward and gave him a full punch in the face, like my mother taught me back home. He really didn't see that coming and then I pulled the key out of the ignition and threw it out of the window. I could see the rage in his eyes, and he grabbed my hair as I tried to scramble out of the van, with instinct I elbowed him in his privates, and he gave out a loud scream. I ran as fast as I could down the road, to get as far away from him as possible. I'm so sorry for being late Mrs Gray." "There's nothing to be sorry for my dear. We are all just extremely glad you are back safe and sound. Now, drink your tea." Mrs Gray was rubbing Lewis' arm and sat with her for a while. Mr Williams heard the whole story with amazement, "I wonder if we will have a delivery tomorrow if he can't find his keys." Mrs Gray laughed as Lewis cracked a smile. "I'm just glad Lewis took care of herself and is safe." Rose continued comforting Lewis as Mrs Gray was called away. Lewis stood up from the table and said to Rose, "where did Hughes go?" Rose replied, "she rushed off in tears." So, they both left the kitchen to find her. They found her in the hallway trying to maintain her composure. She saw Lewis and Rose approaching and burst out crying, "I'm so sorry Lewis, I tried to tell you what he was like. We should have gone with you." Lewis held Hughes in her arms as they both continued sobbing, "I'm alright, now I have found out what he's like. Now he knows me as well. I don't think he will bother us again, no more free lifts for us from now on." The trio began joking about how they will have to use their taxi legs to go between the two locations.

# Chapter 16

# HOME IS WHERE THE HEART IS

Hughes and Lewis were talking about home when Rose came to realise, she had not written back home, and she had now been there twelve days. She picked up a piece of paper from the desk, and as she did Hughes asked if she was going to mention the prince in the letter. Rose closed the question, as she would not know what to put in the letter, she had agreed to return to Arthur. Rose sat there staring at the blank page for a while, thinking, before putting pen to paper.

---

*Dear mum and dad*

*I hope all is well with everyone. It is taking longer than expected to do the dress. I am having a wonderful time and work with some truly amazing people. I feel like I have known them all my life.*

*You are all in my thoughts.*

*Your loving daughter*

*Rose*

---

Rose put the letter in the envelope, addressed it and applied the stamp ready for posting in the morning. She quietly climbed into her bed as Hughes was fast asleep. Laying there in bed, Rose began thinking of her family in Herefordshire before her thoughts became clouded by the thought of the prince. Her prince, she tried to keep him in her mind as she slowly drifted to sleep, and before she knew it, the morning sun had lit up the room waking them up together. They both went to the bathroom to wash and get ready for the day ahead. Then waited for Lewis in the corridor and the three of them went down to the kitchen for breakfast. They were talking about how nice a walk would be in Green Park as the sun was out. Before they could finish a member of staff came into the kitchen, soaking wet, he told them how it was now pouring with rain out there. Rose, Hughes, and Lewis looked at one another, then Mrs Gray leaned over Rose's shoulder and said, "I'd wrap up girls." Rose was not daunted by the weather, when she was in Hereford she would be out on the farm in all seasons. Hughes on the other hand was dragging her feet, not looking forward to the walk.

All the way to the palace, they chatted and giggled, trying to make most of the time away from the other staff. They found humour in everything they could see, from the paper seller on the street having a pile of papers taller than him, to the fat lady walking her tiny dog. They thought it was most amusing. Rose then saw a lady wearing a fur coat, she stopped Hughes and Lewis, so they could also have a good look at the coat. Rose said, "I am going to have a coat just like that someday." Lewis said how she wanted a new thick fabric nighty with lines in it that she could sleep in. Both Rose and Lewis turned to Hughes and asked her what her desires were. Hughes told them how she desired a rich man to sweep her of her feet. Rose tutted, "You can't wear a man Hughes, it needs to be something to wear." As they approached the side of the palace, Hughes pointed to the soldier standing outside the guard-box and said she would like to wear that and smiled.

The guard smiled back, Rose grabbed Hughes's arm, and told her not to do that, as she could get him into a lot of trouble. "The guards are not allowed to be distracted."

Inside the palace, they went to the sewing room and got straight to work on the dress. Mrs Gray came to say good morning and to critique their work. "Now girls, we have to get this ready for three months' time. Please do not let me down and most importantly, do not let yourselves down. I was the one who promised my girls were as good, if not better, than any outside firm, and that is why we have this job. I have great faith in you girls, great faith. Now it is already Thursday, so we must get down to work." Rose brightened up the moment Mrs Gray said Thursday, as that meant the prince was due back at York House. Rose was sewing the appliqué for the dress, and watching the clock, as the pendulum swung back and forth, time had not passed as quickly as she was hoping. The day seemed to drag but she could not wait for it to finish. When the day was over, Rose made Hughes and Lewis hurry back to York House. Lewis was trying to hold everything she was carrying as steadily as she could, so she did not trip over, "What is wrong with you, Rose? We will be running in a minute." Rose was leading the way and yelled back to Lewis, "I need to get back today. I need to have a bath." Lewis caught her breath before responding, "Oh, I see. I had a week like that last week." Lewis and Hughes then picked up the pace and arrived back at York House, red faced and catching their breath, Rose rushed through the doors. Lewis and Hughes prepared themselves and went for their evening meal, while Rose had a bath and washed her hair. She set it in clips and was hoping it would be dry in time to see the Prince of Wales at seven o'clock. Rose had told Hughes to keep Lewis downstairs for as long as possible so that Lewis would not come up and notice Rose was not in their room.

# Chapter 17

# DON'T GET CAUGHT

Hughes kept the conversation going about daily events, though she was running out of things to talk about with Lewis. She managed to get Lewis to go off-topic when she was talking about Rose. Rose was upstairs, approaching the corridor with caution, to see if the footman was still there. She walked to the prince's door and knocked gently three times. The prince opened the door with a grin on his face, "Well come in wosey posey. How was your day?" Rose slipped into the room keeping her eyes locked with his the entire time. "I will not bore you with my day, sir. How was yours?" The prince closed the door behind them and stood leaning against the wall. "Well, another day with boring meetings and very boring people. I had horrid food to eat and not a lot to drink. For a change, I have to say, I am pleased to be back here. Enough of that. Do you play cards Rose?" Rose shook her head back and forth as the prince continued. "Chess?" Rose shook her head again. "No sir, but I am willing to learn." The prince lifted the chessboard and placed it on the table close to Rose. She could feel the warmth of his breath running down her neck. She began to feel nervous and tucked her hands between her legs. The prince then began explaining the game. "Right, Rose. This is a rook, a knight…" He was going into detail, explaining the rules of chess to Rose, and he was about halfway through, and she still did not know what he was on about. As much as she was trying to figure it out to spend more time with him, it seemed a waste of time to her. She thought the life of a prince was going to be more exciting, she could only think of how he is almost locked away, having to sneak around to do things, just like her. She tried to hide her bored expression as she listened to the prince talking about his meetings and other important people. The closer he got to Rose, she could only focus on his appearance, taking in every detail. She could see the lines in his face. It looked as if at some point, it had been sunburned quite badly. She thought of Fred and his face being wrinkly and old looking as if he was weathered. The prince did not look like this, when she passed him the knight that had fallen off the chessboard to the floor, she noticed that his hands were soft to the touch, and quite small. In fact, he was not very big at all. He had small shoulders, fair hair but Rose noticed small specks of grey showing through. "May I ask you something sir?" The prince looked deeply towards Rose, "Oh please do, Rose." "What would you have been if you weren't a prince?" The prince slowly sat back, "I have no idea. Being a prince is the only life I know. What would you have been if you were not a seamstress?" Rose was hunched forward but looked up at the prince, "I would like to marry a rich man and become a Lady. To live in a big house and have lots of children." The prince laughed at Rose's confession. "I thought you would like to be wild and free and travel and have lots of fun like me." Rose held the chess piece of the king in her hand and told the prince how she would like that more than anything.

As they sat and spoke the prince offered Rose a drink. He poured a small glass of whisky for Rose and watched as she took a sip and shrivelled with disgust from the taste. Rose put it to the side and told the prince how she thought it tasted awful. "Have you ever tried champagne?" he said. "No, of course not." She said, as she was still trying to get rid of the taste of the whisky from her mouth. "It is something I would like to try, I heard that the bubbles go up your nose." The prince enjoyed the innocence of Rose and how everything he has lived with was a new experience to her. He picked up a cup of tea from the table and while holding it in his hand, he helped Rose off the chair and kissed her gently on her forehead. "Will I see you again tomorrow Rose?" Rose was caught up in the moment of his lips touching her forehead and breathed, "Yes sir, if you would like sir. Shall I come here at the same time?" The prince, still holding Rose's hand, gazed at her tentatively, "No Rose. I would like you to come here at six-thirty, not seven. Rose shook her head, "yes sir, I will sir." The prince kissed her hand and asked Rose to call him David. "My family and friends call me David, and I am sure Rose we will become good friends." "Of course, sir. I mean David, sir." The prince smiled and said goodnight to Rose as she was leaving the room. Rose checked to make sure there was no one in the corridor, and then snuck away swiftly through the corridor to get to the stairs to head back to her room.

# Chapter 18

# SHE'S IN LOVE

Rose collapsed on her bed and pulled the cover over herself thinking about the prince, David, Prince David. How his friends and family call him David. How she is now seen as a friend. Rose could not sleep properly with all the excitement and happiness she was feeling. When it was time to get up, she was quite miserable and tired. Hughes said to Rose to get up and get dressed, as it was time for breakfast, but Rose waved them away and told them to head on without her. Hughes met Lewis outside the bedroom door and said to her that Rose would catch them up.

They were in the kitchen just finishing off their breakfast when Rose entered. Lewis almost spat her tea back into the cup, "You don't look too good this morning Rose. Feeling under the weather again?" Rose told Lewis that it was just the wrong time of the month and that she would be all right later on. They were walking to the Palace, Rose was waking up to the fresh air brushing her face, making it tingle. When they arrived, they did the same routine and went straight to the sewing room where Mrs Gray was waiting for them. Rose caught Mrs Gray's attention. "You do not look well today my girl. What is the matter?" Lewis interrupted Mrs Gray to say it was the wrong time of the month. Mrs Gray moved towards Rose, "Have you eaten anything this morning?" Rose told her she had not felt like eating or drinking anything. Mrs Gray turned and hastily left the room. In what seemed like a few minutes, she reappeared with a cup of tea for Rose. "Now take it steady today, I know the dress is needed as soon as possible, I would prefer your best work, than you rushing and making a mistake. Rose told Mrs Gray that she would do her best, Hughes looked at Rose shaking her head in an unapproving manor.

At the end of the day, all three of them headed back to York House, tension could be felt between Hughes and Rose. Lewis, oblivious to the reason for Rose feeling so tired, thought she was the cause of the silence. "What a day. I have not had a day like that before. Have I done something to upset you both?" She asked. Rose knocked down Lewis' worry, "No. It is me. I felt miserable this morning and that is what it is." Hughes fumed, "do you think more sleep will solve your problem? "I am sorry," Rose said to Hughes and Lewis.

Back at York House, the three of them sat and had tea together. Rose knew she had to be with the prince at six-thirty but did not want to leave the table before Lewis and Hughes. They finished tea and Hughes suggested they went for a walk for them to unwind. Lewis jumped at the chance to spend more time with Hughes and Rose. Rose knew this would be an effective way to get Hughes and Lewis out of the picture so she could see the prince. She declined the offer of going for a walk, stating that she would give it a miss this time. Lewis told Rose she hopes she feels better soon, and Hughes said, "Rose, try and get an early night." Hughes and Lewis were heading to the door as Rose snuck behind them to leave the kitchen and head upstairs. She looked through the gap of the door and saw the prince standing there in the corridor, as if he was waiting for her, waving her to come in. "Where have you been?" he asked, "I said six-thirty." Rose could not stop apologising for being late. Upon entering the prince's room, she could see he seemed agitated, pacing around with no place to go. "I don't like it when someone's late, Rose," he barked. Rose felt guilty but was not sure why he was behaving like that. "I have apologised, sir. It is difficult to get away from the others without them knowing what I am doing." He looked at Rose and then turned to look at the door. A moment of silence passed, and Rose was not sure whether he wanted her to leave but she could not make herself leave, knowing the prince was ruffled. A sigh from the prince broke the silence, "I want you to take a look on my bed, Rose." Rose's head turned sharply towards the prince, "Why?" she asked. "Good god woman," he said sternly, "go and look on the bed."

Rose was quite startled by the change in his manor.

Rose stood up and walked towards the bed, as she got closer, she felt a little nervous, not knowing why the prince was behaving the way he was. On the bed, she saw a long white box with a blue ribbon tied with a triple bow. She had never seen anything presented so pretty and turned to look at the prince, she smiled with blushing red rosy cheeks. "Go on, open it," the prince demanded. Rose pulled at the ribbon that fell across the box. When she opened it, a gasped silenced filled the room. A fur coat, folded in two, was waiting for her in the box. "For Pete's sake, pick the bloody thing up and see what you think." Rose grabbed it with both hands and pulled it towards her chest, holding it, caressing it whilst taking a deep breath, smelling the freshness of the new fur coat. "Oh, it's lovely sir." Rose put it on, covering her from neck, down her back and towards the floor. It was a bit too big for Rose, but she did not care. This was the very thing she had wanted for such a long time. She swayed side-to-side, walking towards the prince, forgetting the royal protocol and threw her arms around him, thanking him for the gift. The prince could not do anything else but smile. "So, you like it then?" With her arms held tightly around the prince, Rose looked at the prince and replied, "Like it? I love it. It's the greatest present anyone has ever given me."

During the evening with the prince, Rose could not help but stroke the fur coat before putting it on and dancing around the room. Cuddling the prince and thanking him, time and time again. Rose wondered what would happen with her coat when it was time to head back to her room. Would it stay with the prince, would she get to take it with her? Rose did not want the evening to end but it was time for her to go. The prince placed his hands on Rose's waist and gently squeezed and pulled her towards him, he kissed her on the lips. Rose did not push him away but followed his actions, squeezing as tight as she could, against his body. They stood, holding one another for what seemed like minutes.

A whisper from Rose left her lips, "I must go now." Rose looked up at the prince, "Are you here tomorrow evening David?" The prince gazed into Rose's eyes, "Yes, Rose. I will see you tomorrow, but it needs to be around eight o'clock. No later." She leaned in and kissed him on the cheek. "I will be here" she promised. Rose headed back to her room with the fur coat. She entered the room with the coat and stared at it for a few moments, not knowing if this had all been a dream, then realising Hughes was asleep in her bed. "Wake up Hughes." Rose began shaking her sleeping friend. "Look what I have." Hughes sat up waiting for her eyes to focus to the light of the room. "What is it, are you alright?" She asked. Rose nodded, "Look what David has bought me." Hughes could not believe her eyes. Grabbing hold of the coat, Rose pulled it away from Hughes. "A fur coat, you've got a fur coat. Did you call him Prince David? You be careful Rose. Very careful. What did you have to do to the prince to get a fur coat?" Rose corrected Hughes, "Actually, it's a full-length fur coat and I didn't do anything." Rose kept stroking the coat and continued,

"He kissed me tonight, on the lips and held me close to his body with a passion I have never felt before. I could feel the love he had for me, and I think I might love him back with the same passion." Hughes stood up from her bed, "What are you going to do with this? I mean, where are you going to put it? It has to be hidden Rose, so no one can see it. Especially not Lewis. You know if she finds out she will tell everyone Rose. I am keeping a diary of your events and everything that is going on. I have never witnessed anything like this before and do not want to ever forget our lives together. Do not miss a single detail. Not one. I hope that's alright?" Rose gleamed, "A diary of the prince and little old me. You never know, I might be the next princess. He is of an age where he needs a wife, or he will be past it." Rose and Hughes could not help but bubble together. "You know, I have heard the King and Queen would like him to settle down and have a family and it could be with me." Rose kept repeating the same thing over and over about how the prince held her waist and kissed her so gently and bought her the fur coat. "Do you think he's in love with me Hughes?" Hughes expressed her impression, "I have no idea, but you have to remember, he can have any princess in the world, so if I was you, I would be very careful. Men like him don't love that easy, otherwise he would already be married." Rose was not too sure what Hughes was trying to imply with her comments, she took hold of her fur coat and put it in the bed with her and said goodnight to Hughes. Holding the coat against herself, and thinking of the prince, thinking how she had never felt this happy before, even when she was married to Fred.

Rose woke several times in the night to make sure she still had hold of her fur coat. When the morning came, she began panicking. "Hughes, my coat has gone. Where is it, what have you done with it?" Hughes quickly responded, "Woah, calm down Rose. It is at the end of your bed. You must have become too hot in the night with it and pushed it down there." Rose quickly pulled it back towards her, and then put it out of sight just in case someone came into the room. Once she had got herself ready for the day, Rose skipped down to the kitchen and greeted everyone individually and wished them a wonderful day. The staff had thought she had gone mad as it was a working day and it was still early in the morning, but they wished her a good day in return. Rose, Hughes, and Lewis, walked to the Palace. "Right girls. Today we need to get as much of the sewing done as possible and I am going to ask Mrs Gray if we will be able to see Queen Mary in the dress when it is finished. What do you think?" Hughes and Lewis turned to one another and looked back at Rose and told her they thought it was a great idea but only if it was Rose who was the one to ask Mrs Gray. As they entered the Palace, Hughes caught the eye of the Guardsman in the box. He looked straight at her which made her smile as she quickly passed him. "I didn't look at him too long, Rose, but I think there is something there. He has looked at me twice and he had to turn his head to do that. Tomorrow, I will give him a note." Lewis interrupted Hughes, "You can't do that. Folks will see what you are doing, and you will both get into a lot of trouble." Rose thought for a moment before blurting, "We need a distraction." Lewis did not hesitate to agree, "I know, I will walk by him and pretend to faint. He will rush out of his box just before I fall, to catch me and then Hughes, you can slip him the note." Hughes and Rose erupted with laughter, "I think you have seen too many films at the cinema." Said Hughes." We need something a little more subtle." Rose hesitated. "We could come in the other end and drop something close to him. Lewis and I could pick it up and then Hughes, you slip the note to him."

All afternoon, Hughes could not stop thinking of the Guardsman as Rose could not stop thinking of the prince. Lewis kept suggesting ways of getting the Guardsman's attention when Mrs Gray overheard their plans. "And, which Guardsman would that be, may I ask?" Hughes stood up presenting herself to Mrs Gray. "He's the one that stands in the box near to the side entrance. He seems sweet on me, and I would like to say hello." Hughes lowered her head, thinking she was going to be in trouble for trying to distract the Guardsman as Mrs Gray let her stiff expression relax. "Well, I suggest you give me that note, and I shall pass it to him. That way, neither of you will get into any trouble." Rose and Lewis looked at each other with a shocked expression, that Mrs Gray was helping them with a man. Hughes lifted her head with the biggest smile. "Thanks Mrs Gray." Mrs Gray reminded them why they were there, and taking a look at the dress, she could see it was progressing beautifully and was very pleased. She was satisfied with the pattern of applique and also the fine stitches on every piece of fabric that had been sewn onto the dress. Over the fabric, intricate lace had been added which gave the dress a glistening effect.

During their lunch break, Hughes asked Rose and Lewis what she should write in the note. Rose suggested writing her name and a place to meet him when he was off duty. Lewis suggested he should take Hughes out to lunch as he was on a good earner and would have plenty of money. One of the Footmen, George, suggested that she should ask Mrs Gray or Mr Williams if Hughes could invite him into the kitchen for a cup of tea, and then they could all meet him. "That is a great idea, George. Especially after what Lewis went through with Fred. I will ask Mrs Gray and see what she says." Hughes got up and rushed to find Mrs Gray. George looked at Rose and said, "I was only joking, but if it works then problem solved."

he smiled and returned to his duties. Hughes found Mrs Gray and Mr Williams as they were together chatting in his office, she asked them for their approval and permission. Both were in agreement and thought it was a promising idea, Mrs Gray offered her sitting room for the two of them to meet, but only for ten minutes. Mr Williams asked for the note and said he would pass it to the Guardsmen when he changed shift, so there would be no distractions to the other guards while they were on duty. Hughes beamed with excitement and rushed back to the kitchen to tell everyone. Mr Williams wondered what Mrs Gray had been feeding the girls as they seemed so cheerful. Rose had picked herself up from the last time he saw her, and Hughes moved around the kitchen with a spring in her step. He asked Mrs Gray "what has Cook been putting in the food, and could I have some?" Mrs Gray replied, "I could do with some myself. I've forgotten what it's like to be young and in love." Mrs Gray quickly recovered her composure, she asked him if there was someone to assist her with the removal of the curtains in the bedrooms, as they needed to be cleaned.

With all the excitement Rose and Hughes were feeling it helped the day to pass quickly. Mr Williams had passed the note to the Guardsman and Hughes was awaiting a reply impatiently. Rose was eager to get back to York House to be with 'her' prince. Lewis could see the two of them were cheerful, she could understand why Hughes was like this but not Rose. "I overheard Mrs Gray and Mr Williams talking about how happy we all are, especially you too, as they said you were both in love. So come on Rose, out with it. Who are you in love with?" Rose looked at Lewis, "I'm not in love with anyone, that's nonsense. I am happy because I have heard from my family, and they are all well. Nothing more than that." Hughes then chirped in, "I'm not in love either. I'm nervous and excited about the Guardsman, but nothing more. No different to how you were with Fred. You were keen but not in love, weren't you?" Lewis sunk into herself and mumbled, "No, I suppose not." Rose linked arms with them both and told them to get a move on before it gets dark. She knew she had to curb her actions, not to give any evidence of anything happening.

## Chapter 19

# I DON'T WANT TO MISS A THING

At York House, Rose and Hughes went to their room. Rose checked on her fur coat at the back of the small wardrobe to make sure it was still there and had not been touched. "Oh Hughes, I think, I am in love with the prince. My toes curl every time I see him, I cannot stop thinking about him. I think he's fallen in love with me too. I need to learn to speak better than I do, he speaks so well. He uses the word darling a lot, and did I tell you, he calls me wosey posey? When he put his hands on my waist and told me how small it was, I think he liked it. I must not gain an inch." Rose continued babbling on whilst Hughes was trying to write every word in her diary. "Slow down Rose, I'm trying to write it all down. What did you say after darling?" Rose stopped revealing more information for a brief moment. "Do you think it's right to keep a diary on everything we do and say?" she asked. Hughes told her she thinks it's a great idea to keep hold of these memories for many years to come. Rose began repeating what she had already disclosed to Hughes, but Hughes stopped her, "Come on, give me more. Tell me about the way he touched you, the way he kissed you and, of course, what he gave you." Raising her eyebrows. Rose playfully slapped Hughes on the leg, "you are being rude now, it was nothing like that." Rose was looking through her clothes, she had taken her two piece and two summer dresses, she had three pairs of stockings and her underwear, which had seen better days. "Tomorrow, I am going to make myself some new knickers. Do you need any?" she asked Hughes. Hughes thought for a moment and then told Rose that she would also need to knock up a pair of knickers for Lewis, otherwise she would tell. Rose said she was going to ask Mrs Gray if she could use the last silk lining at the end of the roll.

That evening, Rose did her normal thing and sneaked along the corridor to the prince's room; she did not realise she was seen by the footman and the maid, who were having a cuddle in the alcove. The prince opened the door and hurried Rose in. "You can't stay long, I forgot, I have to go out this evening." The prince was dressed in a dark suit, white shirt, and a navy-blue tie. "You look smashing sir." Rose confessed. "Why, thank you Rose." "Can you come to see me tomorrow evening? I am certain I do not have anything on then." Rose was ushered towards the door and quickly passed through the corridor, but not without thinking to herself how she did not have a cuddle or a kiss goodbye from the prince. When she got to her room, Rose was feeling quite miserable, she saw Hughes sat on her bed smiling. "You're back early, was he out?" Hughes asked. Rose slumped onto her bed, "No, he was about to go out though. He said he had forgotten he was going out this evening. He wants me to see him tomorrow instead." Mrs Gray knocked on the door and let herself in and announced, "I have a note for Hughes". Hughes jumped up and took it from Mrs Gray's hand and read it aloud. "I would very much like to have tea with you. I am off on Wednesday if two-thirty is acceptable, then I would very much like to see you then. Please pass Mr Williams your reply. Samual." Mrs Gray expressed her impression of how she thought he seems like a nice young man, and asked Hughes if the time and day were acceptable, and that she would pass the reply to Mr Williams to forward to Samual. As Mrs Gray was leaving the room, Rose stopped her and asked if it was possible for her to have some of the left-over silk lining to make some knickers for her and the girls, as their underwear was practically falling apart. "Is it the pale lime green material?" Mrs Gray asked. "Yes, it is," Rose said. Rose thought that the answer was going to be a no from that question. Mrs Gray said, "Yes, you can have it. It's been there for years. I cannot see anyone ever going to use it." Rose asked Mrs Gray if she would like a pair made, for which she kindly refused; she said, "lime green is not my colour, the dress is your main priority, so you will have to make them in your own time." The next morning, Rose got permission from Mrs Gray to go to the Palace half an hour earlier than usual, so she could make the knickers, asking Hughes and Lewis to join her.

## Chapter 20

# ARE THEY KNICKERS
# OR WALLPAPER?

Hughes, Lewis, and Rose arrived at the Palace and went straight to the sewing room. Lewis had been complaining about how hungry she was as she did not have any breakfast or anything to drink. Rose told her she would ask the kitchen staff if they could do something for her when they had a few minutes to spare. Lewis picked up the fabric for Rose to make the knickers. "Oh, good grief. Is this it? The colour looks like something out of your nose or throat in the morning." Hughes shook her head and Rose asked Lewis if she would still like a pair if the colour of the fabric was that repulsive to her. "Of course, I do. They are only knickers, and no one is going to see mine." Rose and Hughes both replied, "After your date with Fred, I can believe that." The two of them laughed before Lewis burst out with laughter at their response. Rose began measuring Hughes and was asking, "How would you like these? Wide leg, narrow leg, long leg, short leg, loose fit or a tight fit…" Lewis then cut in, "they are only knickers. Rose, would you make mine first?" Rose apologised to Hughes and said, "yes I will make yours first." Lewis requested, "I would like mine wide at the top, wide at the bottom and long in length." Rose began cutting out a pattern on paper, as Lewis was directing her with the size asking for it to be wider and longer and wanting it to be up her back and have everything covered. "Would you like them touching the ground?" Rose joked. At that point, the other staff had begun arriving at the Palace and Mrs Gray came to see how the three of them were getting on. "Rose, what on earth is that? Is it just one pair for the three of you to fit in? You should have a pair you will enjoy wearing, not something that will feel so big and loose on you." Rose cut the legs on the design about half the length but kept the width as Lewis wanted. When they were finished, they looked like old girls' bloomers and not extremely attractive. Hughes then decided she would like a pair of French knickers. Rose was not sure what they looked like; Hughes told her that Page had a magazine with pictures of these knickers which she could look at. The girls continued working on the dress. "Did you ask Mrs Gray if we could see the Queen wearing the dress?" Hughes asked Rose. "Sorry, I completely forgot but I will definitely ask." Rose replied. The three of them were committed to finishing the dress as soon as they could and Hughes was thinking of her upcoming lunch date with the Guardsman, Samual. "What do you think of him girls?" Rose and Lewis could not say much about him as they did not know him, but Lewis piped up "Do you think his head fits that hat, 'cause if it doesn't, he may only be four feet tall." Rose began guessing saying she thinks he is at least five feet tall. Hughes was gushing with excitement, "I do hope he is nice and just the person I am looking for. I feel ready to settle down." Lewis looked at Hughes and asked how many men she had stepped out with. Rose told Hughes she did not need to answer if she felt uncomfortable, but Hughes confessed, "Not many. In fact, he will be the first." Lewis advised Hughes to be careful and if he wanted to make it official on the second date, she had best be careful and think of what happened between her and Fred. "Didn't you mention before about being with someone named Fred, Rose?" Lewis asked. Rose was more comfortable disclosing personal things with Lewis and Hughes and started telling them about him. "I was. We were married but he died a while back, he drowned in the brook. He was poorly and they think he fell in and could not get out. There is also Arthur, but I have only seen him at our local market. He was interested in me and asked me to step out with him. I didn't, or haven't though, as I came here and not seen him since." Rose looked at Hughes to make sure she did not mention anything about the prince in the midst of these confessions, she received a glance back, and a short smile from Hughes, to reassure her that she would not mention the prince.

# Chapter 21

# FRIENDS WITH BENEFITS

Later that evening, Rose was getting herself ready for her visit to the prince's room. "Are you alright covering for me Hughes?" Rose asked. "Of course, just don't forget all the juicy details." Rose walked through the corridors to get to the staircase to go to the prince's room. She tapped on the door and a light from within lit up the hallway. The prince was stood there wearing a smoking jacket with his shirt collar undone, he seemed quite relaxed. "Hello wosey posey," Those were the three words that invited her into the room. The prince was all of a chatter. "How are you this evening Rose?" he asked. "Very well. How are you?" The prince told Rose how he went out the night before, and how it was most interesting to him. He had met some wonderful people. He sat close to Rose and put his hand on her thigh and started kissing her neck. He held her closer and breathed, "Oh wosey." Rose was unsure what to do, she was enjoying every kiss. They echoed through her entire body, like an electric pulse. The princes' hands began to wander as if they had a mind of their own, he was still focusing his kisses on to her neck. She leant back slightly and did nothing. The prince felt that Rose was not at ease and stopped. Sitting upright, he asked if Rose felt all right with him kissing her. "You don't mind, do you? I just want to hold you close to me and feel your skin against mine," he said. Rose felt that this was something she also wanted, as her heart was racing aloud. "David, I am yours, if that is what you want." He took her by the hand and led her into the bedroom. He slowly undressed her whilst moving his hands softly around her body, removing every piece of fabric covering her, she climbed back onto the bed showing her naked self to the prince. He joined her on the bed, touching her before she stopped him abruptly, telling him she had not done this for a long time, and did not want to get it wrong. "To get it wrong, Rose!" said David surprised. "I feel a little confused, you know when you meet someone and then all of a sudden you have so many feelings you do not know what to do. Do you understand?" Rose said. David looked more confused than ever, he wondered what thoughts were going through her mind, as he had never experienced anything like this before. The prince asked Rose to leave. Rose dressed quickly and left the room, feeling sorry for herself but wondering what was going on with him, as this was not normal behaviour, not from any man. Rose went back to her room and Hughes was there waiting to hear about her evening. "Gone out again has he Rose?" She asked. Rose was still puzzled by her encounter with him that evening, "Not quite, but get your diary out. I will tell you everything that just happened and see if you can make any sense of it." After Hughes heard what Rose had to say, she wrote it all down, she asked if he could be one of those creepy people that just look but never touches. "I hope not." Rose hesitated, "Do you think he thinks I am too thin? He did mention how thin I was the first night he kissed me, and he had his hands around my waist." Hughes asked Rose if she were going to see him the following night, Rose told her the prince had not asked her, but she would go to his room and ask him what was going on.

It was Wednesday morning and Hughes was extremely anxious about her meeting in Mrs Gray's room with Samual, later that day. Hughes was allowed to stay at York House and finish some things that needed mending, Rose and Lewis went to the Palace as usual. Rose and Lewis found that the day passed a little slower than usual without the bubbly personality from Hughes. They were sewing the curtains as Mrs Gray didn't want them to work on the dress without Hughes. The three of them had their own individual needle skills that made the dress standout the way it did. It was unheard of for someone to be given time away from their job to meet another member of the Palace staff. Mrs Gray knew a distant member of Samual's family, and allowed them to meet, Samual could be sent to another post at short notice, and anyway Mrs Gray was an old romantic at heart.

Samual looked different as he was not in uniform when he came to Mrs Gray's sitting room to meet Hughes. He was dressed very smart, standing tall in his tweed jacket and dark grey trousers. He entered the sitting room that Mrs Gray had prepared for the two of them to meet. Samual was just as nervous as Hughes. "Good afternoon, I am Samual." Hughes brightened up, knowing that he was just as excited as she was to meet him. "Hello, my name is Jean, but here everyone calls me Hughes." She blushed. Samual wanted to let Hughes know that he was not just a member of staff, he really liked her too, so he asked Hughes if she would mind if he called her Jean. With her hands behind her lower back, Hughes bit her bottom lip and nodded to Samual's request. The two of them began talking, knowing that they did not have much time to enjoy each other's company. Jean told Samual how Rose and Lewis thought he would be shorter. Samual told her that it is the hat that makes them look like they have no body, just a head on legs. Jean was laughing at Samual's jokes with a hint of nervousness, although as time passed, she felt more confident in front of him. They discussed where they were both from, what their families were like. Jean was curious about Samual's family and his military background. Samual was polite and well-mannered towards her. Jean felt uncomfortable to tell him how her family were in service, but he always found a way to keep it positive, telling her that it was great she was working for the Royal Household. Their time together was ending, and Samual asked Jean if he could see her again on the Saturday and take her to lunch. She wanted to jump at the chance to say yes, but did not want to seem to eager, after what Lewis went through with Fred. Samual also said, "Please bring a friend if you don't want to come alone." On this, Jean asked "what time?" "12:30 he replied." She excepted his invitation, and as Samual made his way to the door, he said "I will meet you by the palace gate then 12:30." As he walked away, he turned to Jean, gave a gentle wave, and smiled.

Hughes stayed at York House for the remainder of the day, continuing to sew and mend what needed doing, finishing one thing after another with no distractions. She waited for Lewis and Rose to return, finishing her work, and greeted them with the biggest hug and smile. Rose was about to ask how it was before Hughes answered her unspoken question. "He was amazing. He was dressed so smart and was funny, polite, and so wonderful. Oh, he is also a lot taller without the hat." Lewis was still a bit sceptical after being bitten and hurt by love and romance, herself. "You were only with him for a brief time, and you feel that way towards him, but he might be like Fred, awful." Hughes looked at Lewis with disappointment, she was trying to be resilient to Lewis's response. "Please do not spoil it for me Lewis. I have never had anyone interested in me before. I even told him about my family being in service and he didn't seem to mind. I think there could be something there." Hughes took in a breath and absorbed her feelings toward Samual. She then asked, "How was your day girls?" Rose decided she would quickly respond to Hughes, so that

Lewis could not say anything else that may dampen the day. "Nothing exciting happened, it has been quiet without you. We were just sewing the old curtains again," Lewis cringed, "I am sick and tired of sewing bloody old curtains. You think with all their money they would buy new ones and throw away the old ones." The three of them continued to talk about their day whilst getting ready for their tea.

Rose and Lewis were enjoying eating their tea, but Hughes was picking at hers. Lewis was staring at her plate of food, "If you're not going to eat it, can I have it?" Hughes passed the plate across to Lewis, and then offered the bread for Lewis to mop-up the gravy. After clearing that plate of food, she said to Hughes, "that should see me through to the morning." She then asked Hughes and Rose if they wanted to go for a walk, her belly was full, and this would help shift the gas. That comment made Hughes chuckle as Rose cringed at the thought, "You will never have to worry about being a lady, Lewis." Hughes and Lewis began to laugh which then caused Lewis to burp. "Oh my god, that's disgusting." Rose stood up and left the table, leaving Hughes and Lewis looking at one another before they themselves, got up from the table to go for their walk.

Rose was in her bedroom, she opened the door and looked out along the corridor, making sure no one was outside before closing it and putting a chair up against the back of it. This would stop anybody from entering and surprising her. She opened the wardrobe and pulled out the box with her fur coat inside. She placed it on her bed and opened it, admiring her dream in a box and that it was just for her. She rubbed her hands through the fur with her fingers open, with soft fur gracefully wrapping around each finger as her hand passed over it. She put the coat on and stretched out her arms one at a time, to see if she was growing into it for it to be a perfect fit. After a few minutes, Rose put the coat back in the box and then hid the box in the back of the wardrobe. She then closed the wardrobe doors, pushing them tight before turning around to pick up her dress, underwear, and clean stockings. She removed the chair from the back of the door, walked to the bathroom to run a bath so she could soak in the water for a little while. Once she had finished in the bathroom, she felt fresh and relaxed, ready to see the prince to find out what happened the other night, during that moment of passion. She knew the prince was not expecting her that evening but still made the decision to approach him.

## Chapter 22

# IT'S NOW OR NEVER

Walking down the corridor at eight-thirty, Rose tapped on his door, not knowing what reaction she would get from the unexpecting prince. The door opened with the prince wearing pyjamas and a smoking jacket, not a dressing gown, Rose thought this was an odd combination. "Come in Rose, do come in. We cannot have people seeing you outside my door." Rose thought that was strange as he did not call her wosey posey like he usually does. He was not his jovial self. He closed the door behind Rose before announcing, "I want to tell you something Rose. This can go no further, do you understand?" Rose was nervous about what she was going to hear, "Of course sir, I mean, David, my lips are sealed." He went on to tell her how he was not feeling up to doing much that day. "You see Rose, I have met someone. This woman who makes my heart flutter every time I see her." Rose felt he must be thinking about her, or was there someone else, she listened with intent. The prince continued telling Rose about his feelings towards this woman, "What do you think I should do? Should I tell her? Should I send flowers and buy her gifts?" Rose could not understand why the prince was telling her. Especially as they were intimate with one another, sneaking around most evenings, she bit her tongue, hoping it was her, about whom he was talking. Her thoughts were obstructed by the thought that it could be for someone else and responded with, "Of course you should tell her. Buy her

96

gifts and always send flowers, as many as possible. They are a sign of giving someone your heart." Rose stood to attention knowing that she had to be professional in this moment. The prince was walking from wall to wall in the room before turning to Rose, "By golly, you are right. Come with me." He took Rose by the hand and led her to the bedroom and told her to get undressed and get into bed. Rose did not know what to do, so she did as she was told. She slipped beneath the covers, and he joined her; Breathing heavily, the heat of the prince's breath was warming Rose's neck and chest which made her enjoy it more. His hands caressing her curvy body, and when the prince had finished bouncing Rose around, he climaxed, Rose pulled the cover higher to hide her cheeky smile. The prince turned on his back. Catching his breath, he lit a cigarette and exhaled the smoke, "You can go now Rose. Thank you for your advice." Rose paused for a moment, not knowing if he was serious or if it was his way of making a joke. There was no other response from the prince whilst he was laid in the bed, puffing on his cigarette, looking as though he had done a day's work. Rose slowly got out of bed and began dressing when the prince leant over and kissed her on the bottom. She jumped forward, still confused by the whole encounter and quickly pulled herself together before heading out of the bedroom. She went down the corridor straightening her clothes, trying to put reason to what had just happened.

Rose arrived back at her room and was alone as Hughes and Lewis were still out on their walk. She let out a little burst of tears that she had been holding in the entire time she was with the prince. Rose was not sure if it was tears of happiness or sadness. Rose waited for Hughes to come back to tell her everything. She heard whispers in the corridor and knew it was Hughes. She could hear Hughes was saying to Lewis that Rose must be asleep by now, and we will speak in the morning at breakfast. Hughes quietly opened the door, not to disturb Rose and saw Rose was standing there with a smirk on her face. Hughes then burst in and quickly closed the door behind her, "Well, how did it go tonight? Was he there?" Rose took Hughes by the hands and sat her down next to her. "He made love to me." Hughes's eyes sprung open; her mouth dropped to the floor with a gasp. Rose continued "I know, he loves me. He kept mentioning about his feelings towards this woman that makes his heart flutter every time he sees her, and then he took me to the bedroom and made love to me. The prince took me into the bedroom and told me to get into bed. He then climbed in naked next to me and took hold of me. The bed started shaking and then it was over. You see that woman has got to be me. He bought me the fur coat and he made love to me. If he buys me another gift, that is enough to know that it is me he is in love with." Hughes and Rose were bouncing with excitement, about what Rose and the prince got up to. Rose saying that this is the life she was meant to have. To live in a place like this with a prince. Hughes was writing everything down in her diary, and as she was doing this, she said to Rose "be careful and to think about what you are doing." Rose brushed off Hughes's words; they were only envy for what she has with the prince.

# Chapter 23

# IS THAT FOR ME?

A few weeks had passed, at the Palace the dress was getting closer to completion. Rose picked up the courage to ask Mrs Gray if the three of them could see her Majesty wearing the dress when it was finished. Mrs Gray had to tell them that it wouldn't be possible, the Queen would only take a fitting with the designer. You will be able to see the dress on a photograph or painting of the Queen at a later date. Rose was not to upset by what Mrs Gray said, through her own thoughts she would see the Queen on a regular basis when she became a member of the family. As she truly believed that her prince, David, was so in love with her.

That evening, Rose went to see David in his room, she tapped on the door, he opened it. He was admiring a ring in a black velvet box, it glistened. He held it out to show her, "What do you think of this Rose?" Her eyes lit up and she began to stutter. The prince proceeded, "I know, quite small, the emerald's quite small." The prince closed the lid on the box and held it out to Rose. "It's yours Rose, you can have it, I will get the bigger one tomorrow." Rose took the box and opened it, to look at it again, as she admired it, she said, "It's beautiful." The prince smiled at Rose's reaction, "Right, you have to go now, as I have someone important to see this evening." Rose held the box securely in her hand and rushed back to her room. Hughes was just coming out of the door of the room, Rose grabbed her arm and pulled her back in, "Come with me!" she exclaimed. Rose opened the box presenting the ring to Hughes. "Do you believe me now? A ring for me, he really does love me." Rose pulled it from the box and tried putting it on her finger, but it didn't fit. Hughes suggested, "try it on another finger." And then said, "Anyway you can't wear it here. Everyone will want to know how you could afford a ring like that, or they may think you have stolen it." Rose agreed and said she would not say anything about the ring until David was ready. Hughes was incredibly open minded about everything; She could see that Rose had a blinkered attitude towards what she was getting herself into. Why would a prince, which could one day be their king, fall for a servant girl seamstress like Rose? "Why didn't he take the ring back to get the right size Rose?" Hughes questioned her. Rose shrugged off the negative attitude that Hughes was giving, "I do not know. He was in a hurry; he had to see some friends and practically threw it at me. However, he did say he was going to get me a bigger one tomorrow, so I did not say anything." Rose put the ring back in the box and closed it putting the box into her pocket. Hughes said, "I am just about to go for a walk with Page, Lewis, and Smith, would you like to come along?" "Yes" she replied, "I will just grab my coat." Hughes advised Rose to hide the ring somewhere that it would not be found. As she went out the door she said, "We will wait for you by the back door, don't be long." Rose opened the box to her fur coat, and before placing the black velvet box into the pocket of the coat; she took one final look at the ring and smiled.

The five ladies left York House and walked through Green Park towards Hyde Park Corner. Rose always enjoyed the walk through the park as it reminded her of being in the countryside. She did not join in with the conversations the other four were having, as her mind was pondering on the ring.

Page spoke about a magazine she had just read, saying it had lots of fashion tips about everything, not only on clothes, but makeup too. She spoke about the underwear including the new French knickers and that there was a pattern of how to make them. Rose perked up, "Can I have a look? I am making knickers at the moment; I will make you a pair if you lend me the magazine. They will be green, lacy, and provocative." The four ladies looked at Rose, and giggled with surprise, they had never heard this side of her before, describing underwear in that way. After they finished walking through the Park, laughing, and enjoying each other's company, they began making their way back to York House. The conversations never ran thin when they were all together. Smith asked if any of them had heard any gossip about the prince. Rose tugged on Hughes's jacket thinking she may have told someone her secret. Before either of them could change the conversation, Lewis asked, "What gossip?" Smith turned to the four of them and began spilling her gossip. "Well, I have heard he's got a new woman in tow, and he is smitten." Rose lifted her eyes to look at Hughes with a grin on her face. "No, I haven't heard that. Do you know who it is?" Lewis begged. Smith shook her head, "no, but I am sure we will find out soon." Rose wanted to scream out that it is her, but she knew she could not say anything, not even to her closest friends. They all enjoyed being the person with the story to tell at the palace. Hughes moved the conversation on to her and Samual, as they continued walking back to the house. Page then told them about her boyfriend, how he worked long hours at the colliery, and that when they could afford it, she would marry him. Smith made it clear that she had no intention of ever getting married. She was more than happy to live out her days in service. Stating how she had everything she needed to live; she had her room, her clothes, food, and friends. Rose did not react to Smith's statement, she just said how the evening was getting colder and how she felt tired, they needed to hurry the walk so she could get back.

Friday morning. Page had passed the magazine to Rose, and she took it with her to the palace. In the sewing room, she copied the pattern from the magazine on to paper and cut it out. Rose held the pattern up to show Hughes and Lewis. Lewis thought the size of the pattern was too small, they would be tight and would not cover much. Hughes said, "if you sew a pair up, I will try them on." Rose searched through the spare materials in the sewing room, she was looking for a piece of fancy lace, so she could make the knickers look like the ones in the magazine. Mrs Gray entered the sewing room wishing them all a good morning. Rose reciprocated and asked if there was any spare lace she could have, to dress the knickers with. The three ladies stood there waiting for Mrs Gray's response, she tilted her head and looked at an old box on top of the cabinet in the corner of the room. She said, "there may be some lace in that box up there, it's full of old material from Victorian days. Rose and Hughes lifted the box off the top of the cabinet, brushing off the layer of dust. Hughes opened it carefully and could see lots of historic cloth and trim. "Just think these would have been applied to the late Queen Victoria's dresses," Rose said. Lewis was captivated by Rose's reaction after seeing what was within, amazed by the amount of lace that was there. Lewis asked Rose if she could also make a pair of knickers for her. Holding up a length of corded lace, she said, "can I have some of this lace on mine." Rose replied, "yes you can, but you will have more lace than knickers with that. I have to make up the others first." Hughes laughed to think that that lace on their knickers would be older than all of them. Mrs Gray was impressed by the creativity Rose had in placing the lace on to the knickers, reminding them all it was time to carry on with the dress. Mrs Gray left the room, while Hughes and Lewis carried on working on the dress. Rose said she could get a pair of knickers made within minutes and ran them up on the treadle machine. She finished them off by sewing the lace to the top of the fabric. Rose held out a pair of knickers and said to Hughes, "I made these up for you, you said you would try them on." Hughes lifted her dress just above her knees and then slipped on the knickers, one leg at a time, pulling them up to her waist. Rose and Lewis were curious as to how they felt, "did the lace tickle," Lewis asked. Hughes lifted her dress, revealing the knickers. "Oh my!" Lewis choaked. "They are very short, but the lace looks ever so pretty." Hughes pulled her dress back down and took off the knickers. Lewis, remarked to Rose, "please could you make mine a bit longer." Rose replied, "they are French knickers, not bloomers!

# Chapter 24

# A DRESS FIT FOR A QUEEN

Later that afternoon, Queen Mary's dress was finished. Mrs Gray was amazed with the dress, and proud of what her girls had accomplished together. She could not wait for Her Majesty's lady in waiting, to collect the dress, to see her reaction. Rose, Hughes, and Lewis were summoned to Mrs Gray's room, the three of them were wondering what they must have done wrong; had they made a mistake or was the dress not to the approval of the Queen. "I have something I must say about this dress to you all," Mrs Gray said sternly, as the three of them slightly lowered their heads. "You have all done an excellent job. It is unfortunate you will not see the dress on Her Majesty, but you must be proud in knowing the outstanding work you have done for our Queen. Many do not have the skills or the opportunity to do what you have done. So, well done. That will be all." Lewis and Hughes sighed with relief, but Rose began to rock back and forth feeling faint. Mrs Gray and Hughes held onto Rose from both sides and guided her to a chair. "I do not know how many times I have to tell you girls. You must eat breakfast, or you will make yourselves ill." Rose was not too sure what caused her to feel faint, she explained to Mrs Gray that she did have breakfast, and that it may be because of the excitement of completing the dress?

It was time for the three friends to begin making their way back to York House. Lewis was walking ahead greeting everyone she passed with positive vibes from being a young lady who had just finished a dress for the Queen of England. Hughes was walking cautiously with Rose, in case she was going to faint, she kept highlighting that the fresh air would do her good. Rose feeling sick, did not want to embarrass herself or the others, by being sick publicly. She began hurrying on to the house, gagging, as she barged past Lewis. When they arrived back at York House, Rose ran to the bathroom feeling that she was going to vomit. Hughes waited by the bathroom door for Rose to emerge. After a brief time, Rose opened the door with tears running down her face. "I think I will go and have a lie down for a while," she said. Hughes kept saying that there must be a sickness bug, or she must have eaten something that was not cooked properly, but Rose had other ideas in her mind. She remembered feeling the exact same way when she was pregnant with Jim.

Hughes helped Rose get into bed before leaving. Rose waited for several minutes before she got back out of it, she looked for a small bottle in the large drawer of the dressing table, oil of cloves. This would help relieve the symptoms of sickness when she felt poorly. She rummaged through, pushing things side-to-side, reaching into the back of the draw to find it. She could see the monthly rags that she had brought from home, folded neatly at the bottom of the drawer which was a reminder in her thoughts that she could be pregnant.

The next day was not like any other day. Rose was not thinking about the prince, her friends, or the work on the dress she had done. All she could think about was being pregnant. She was unsure of whom she could confide in. She trusted Hughes, but could Hughes provide the answers she needed at this time, this needed more than a friend's trust. An unmarried mother would be rejected in society, and this was nothing she had planned for. She kept going over different scenarios in her mind, how she could tell her parents and Arthur. How will the prince respond, it could only be his? He was the only man she had been with since her late husband, Fred.

The next morning, Hughes had kept her distance from Rose to ensure she did not catch anything that Rose might be carrying. She popped into the bedroom now and again to check on her, taking a cup of tea. "How are you feeling now?" Hughes asked. Rose did not feel that she could tell Hughes what was causing her sickness, so told her that she was feeling a little better. "Are you sure you are feeling better or are you going to be ill for a full nine months," Hughes teased. Rose shrieked by Hughes's comments. "What are you saying, Hughes?" "Well, let us be honest Rose. You have not washed your rags and hung them to dry since you arrived here, and I've done mine several times." Rose slumped onto the corner of the bed, looking up at Hughes with fear in her eyes. "What the hell am I going to do?" She wept. "How am I going to tell him?" Hughes sat beside Rose and pulled her into her shoulder to comfort her. "I don't know, but it's not going to go away anytime soon, and you need to go and see him tonight."

Later that evening, around eight-thirty, Rose had tidied herself up to look more presentable, she went along the corridor in search of the prince. She tapped on his door as she usually did and the prince opened it with the greeting, "hello wosey posey." He told Rose he would not be able to entertain her this evening as he had a dinner date he needed to attend. He stood in the doorway wearing a dinner suit, a cigarette loosely hanging from his lip, with the smoke drifting across his face making him close his one eye. "I need to talk to you!" Rose demanded. The prince pulled the cigarette from his mouth, blowing the smoke out into the corridor above Rose's head, "I am afraid it is going to have to wait until tomorrow night, wosey. I will speak with you then." Now, I must be getting ready, goodnight, Rose." He said as the door shut in her face. Rose could tell by his attitude, even before she could tell him she is pregnant, he was not going to be interested. She arrived back at the room full of despair, Hughes was waiting and could see she was upset, so gave her a hug. "Oh Rose, you did not tell him, did you?" Hughes asked. Rose threw her arms up in the air with bewilderment to how impolite David had been towards her. "I could not tell him; I never had the chance to. He told me he was going out to dinner, and that I would have to wait to see him tomorrow." Rose took herself to bed, full of worry about what was to become of her.

# Chapter 25

# TIME'S UP

The next morning, Mrs Gray called for the staff to assemble in the kitchen for an announcement. Rose could not help but panic, was it about her? Had someone heard her and Hughes talking? She knew she had to put on a brave face and attend. "Good morning, ladies. We are moving back across to the Palace at the end of the week as the work at the palace is finished. Please make sure when you pack-up your belongings, the room is left as you found it. Rose, I'm sorry to say that we will no longer be needing your services after this week. I would like to thank you for assisting in making and sewing the appliqué on to the Queens dress." Hughes and Lewis both looked at Rose with sorrow in their face. They had enjoyed working with Rose, her attitude towards life had given them both more confidence. Feelings of sorrow and disappointment were passing through Roses mind, what would be her next step? Her eyes watered, as she realised things were a lot different to when she had arrived at the palace. Mrs Gray came over to Rose and gave her a hug. "I am sorry my dear, but you knew it was only for a brief time." Rose wiped away a tear and composed herself. "Thank you," she said. Mrs Gray told Lewis and Hughes to go across to the palace and repair the curtains she had placed on the sewing table. Rose turned to Mrs Gray, and in a trembling voice, asked if she could go with Hughes and Lewis, to help for one last time. Mrs Gray said, "yes for one last time, you may go with them."

As they walked to the palace Rose glanced at the pigeons flying across their heads, as she inhaled the London air. She thought to herself how she would miss this. She spent the entire day, taking in her surroundings more than usual, admiring the long running carpets, door handles, and large paintings in their gold frames hanging on the walls in the corridors. "Are you alright, Rose?" Hughes asked. "I'm fine, I am just thinking how I will miss all of this, it has been such an adventure?" Lewis looked at Rose and replied, "It has been great working with you, thank you for the underwear. I do not think anyone else would ever have had the nerve to make them, or even the guts to ask Mrs Gray. Since you have been here, I have seen a different side to that old bat. Wouldn't you agree, Hughes?" Hughes nodded in agreement. As they continued sewing the curtains Rose did not look at the time once, she did not want the day to end. "That's it," said Hughes. That is what? Said Lewis. "Time to go back for tea" she replied. All three walked out of the sewing room and Rose looked back for the very last time, before pulling the door shut.

Rose walked in between Hughes and Lewis and lifted her arms around their shoulders, "This has been the most exciting thing that has ever happened to me, you two are more than friends, you are more like sisters. I feel closer to you both than I do my own sister May. I feel so relaxed and comfortable around you both, it is like, I can be whatever I want to be." Lewis looked at Rose, "Are you done, Rose? I do not like people who over-elaborate on things." Rose laughed and playfully nudged Lewis before continuing their walk.

When they got to York House, they were walking through the hallway when a footman approached them. "Have you heard the prince has a woman in tow. He has been seen out in the town flirting with some woman, whom everyone is talking about it." Mr Williams suddenly put his head around the door of his office and told the footman to get back to work or there would be repercussions for gossiping like that. He then voiced his own opinion to say that it was about time that the Prince of Wales had found someone and married. Rose knew that she had extremely limited time to tell the prince she is pregnant. She went to his room that night and knocked on the door for what she could only imagine being the very last time. The door opened, and there stood the prince in his pyjamas and a silk dressing gown. "Come on in wosey posey." She walked past him showing no expression, as she could not tell if he was happy to see her or not. He put his arm around her waist and held her close, this made her troubles disappear in his embrace. He asked her what she was doing, but Rose did not have the chance to say anything before the prince began kissing her on the side of her cheek and onto her neck. He took her by the hand and led her to his bed. He pushed her back onto the bed and rolled her over, her face was in the cover. He lifted her dress up and saw the new green lacy French knickers she had made. "Well, I see you have dressed it for me," he said, he was overly excited at the sight of them and spanked her bottom, she let out a little squeal of surprise. He thrust himself against her bottom, pinning Rose to the edge of the bed. Rose thought she was going to suffocate in the blankets. He was becoming heavier with each thrust and slapped her on the thigh repeatedly, grabbing her clothes and pulling her tighter against him until it hurt. "Stop. Stop!" she cried. He continued thrusting and she used her foot to push him off. "What is wrong? You are no fun tonight. You might as well go now," He fumed. "Rose pushed her dress down and looked at him. "I have something I need to tell you." He could see she had a serious look in her eyes. "What is it?" He questioned. "I am going to have a baby." She explained as he looked shocked. "I'm going to have your baby David, you put it in my belly." The prince paused in disbelief. "It is time you left; you need to leave now! You have ruined it! You have gone and ruined everything!" He raged. Rose ran out of the room crying, not caring who saw her leave the prince's room.

Hughes could hear her sobbing through the corridor as she approached their room, she opened the door to Rose weeping. "Oh, Hughes, he was like a mad man. He hurt me." Hughes was worried about Rose, why, what did he do?" She asked. "He slapped my bottom, at first it felt playful and nice, but he became more aggressive and forceful with each slap. It is stinging a bit." Rose began lifting her dress to show Hughes, but she did not reveal her bottom before Hughes gasped at the sight of the redness down her leg. "I will fetch the calamine lotion, which will cool it." Hughes left the room and ran to get the lotion. Rose sat on the bed waiting on her return. "I told him. I told him I am pregnant, and he said, I have ruined his evening, ruined everything and that I had better leave." Hughes was comforting Rose whilst making notes in her diary. Rose went on explaining how he walked her to his bed, lifting her dress, making a remark about her new knickers, "dressed it for me," he said. Then what felt like passion turned to pain and she forced him off. "It was then that I told him I was pregnant and that's when he had this rage telling me to leave." Hughes put the lotion down and held Rose in her arms. "What am I going to do Jean?" Rose asked. "Rose, you just called me Jean, you can always call me Jean. We call you Rose, so it is only fair."

The next evening, Rose returned to the prince's room, wishing to speak to him about the position she was in. This time there would be no sneaking through the corridor, she knew she did not have anything to lose now her time at the palace was near the end. She knocked on the door with her head held high, but she was not greeted by the prince.

His Private Secretary, Hardinge, stood there in front of her, looking surprised to see a Seamstress standing at the prince's door. "Can I help you?" He asked. Rose was shocked, not expecting to see him there, she knew she could not escape, feeling courageous she said, "I have come to see David." "I beg your pardon! Do you mean Prince Edward?" Hardinge roared. "I do, but he told me to call him David," she prompted. Hardinge was not looking too impressed that Rose was standing there saying this. "And when did the Prince of Wales tell you that you could call him David?" Rose knew that Hardinge was not going to back down easily, so she took a deep breath and bragged, "When he was making love to me in his bed." She continued telling Hardinge everything when the prince rushed to the door. "Hardinge, this is Rose. Now, send her away. I need to make arrangements." Before the prince could finish, Rose queried if those arrangements were for her and their baby she was carrying. The prince pleaded with Rose to come back in the morning around nine-thirty as he was busy, so they could discuss everything. Hardinge said for her not to tell another soul, as he was shocked by what he had just heard. Back at their bedroom, Rose was feeling desperately sad, she chatted with Hughes telling her everything, which she wrote down in her diary.

# Chapter 26

## WHISPERS IN THE HALLWAY

The morning came and Rose was dressed, knowing how anxious she felt, ready for her meeting with the prince; when Mrs Gray called for all the staff to gather in the kitchen. She wanted everyone to say a farewell to Rose as she would be leaving on the Friday. Hughes explained that Rose had an appointment with Mr Hardinge and was certain that she would come back down to the kitchen after their meeting had finished. Mrs Gray was curious, "Well, I cannot see what that is for. They don't usually go to see the Prince's Private Secretary when a member of staff leaves." A footman in the kitchen blurted "Do you think it's because she is the corridor hopper?" Hughes gasped and quickly stepped back behind two other members of staff; Mrs Gray gave a stern look at the footman. "And what on earth does that mean?" She said raising her voice. The footman feeling sheepish for what he just blurted out stepped forward and explained, "You know, when they hop and skip to the prince's room, and then hop all the way back with a smile on their face. I saw Rose on a few occasions sneaking through the corridor, entering his room, and one time she left with this great big box with a ribbon on it." Mrs Gray stepped between the two people that Hughes was hiding behind. "Do you know anything of this Hughes?" She asked. Hughes didn't say anything, looking guilty. Lewis began speaking, "I thought there was something strange happening. All these early evenings and her feeling unwell.

The crying and fainting, it all adds up. Now she is seeing his Private Secretary, come on Hughes, tell us what is going on." All eyes were on Hughes. "I have no idea. I don't know why she is seeing Mr Hardinge, she never said anything to me. I know she was upset having to leave, but that's it. I don't know anything else." Mrs Gray ushered the staff to get back to work and began investigating things herself.

Rose was on her way to her meeting, nervous about what Mr Hardinge was going to say to her. He invited her into the room and asked her to take a seat. He was calm and professional in his manner. It felt strange to Rose as he was acting so differently to the night before. "Now, Rose, if you would like to explain to me what has happened." Rose began to confess some of the things that had happened between her and the prince from the moment they first saw each other. She was finding it difficult to talk about their intimate time together and feelings she had had with the prince. Mr Hardinge told Rose to take her time and offered her a drink to help her clear her throat. Mr Hardinge sat and listened to everything Rose was saying. She told him about the fur coat and the ring, and she went on, she was surprised that he did not seem shocked by what she was telling him. Rose went on to say that she thought he wanted to marry her, as he had given her the ring. When Rose mentioned this, Mr Hardinge sighed, as if this was not the first time, he had heard a saga like this. She told him that she had been feeling ill and then realised that she was pregnant. It could only be the prince's due to time and location of her job at York House. Mr Hardinge took that opportunity to ask how she knew she was pregnant; Rose felt reluctant to explain but knew she had to tell him that she had been suffering from morning sickness and had missed her time of the month, since she had started at the palace. Mr Hardinge leant back in his chair.

"Alright, Rose, I will speak to the prince and see what we can sort out for you." Rose began weeping. "How can I go home in this condition? My family will not take me back like this." Mr Hardinge stood from his chair and put his hand on Rose's shoulder, "Try not to worry Rose. I will see what we can do." Rose stood and bowed her head to Mr Hardinge as a sign of appreciation for what she could see as his help. She then made her way to the kitchen not knowing that Mrs Gray had been questioning the staff about Roses shenanigans at York House.

The kitchen was quiet which was unusual at that time of the morning. Mr Williams and Mrs Gray were waiting for Rose. "Is everything alright Rose?" Mrs Gray asked. Rose was oblivious to what they believed she was up to. "Yes, Mrs Gray, but I don't think I will be able to stay longer than you said." Mr Williams put one foot forward leaning slightly towards Rose with disgust, "So you went to the hierarchy, above Mrs Gray's head to save your job, did you?" Mrs Gray put out her hand to Mr Williams to stop him leaning over Rose. She smiled at Rose, "the girls are in the laundry room down the corridor, go and help them." There is still work to be done while you are here, off you go." Rose was just outside the kitchen door, she overheard Mr Williams talking to Mrs Gray, asking if she found out anything about the rumours going around. Mrs Gray replied that she wasn't sure, but she knew Rose liked working here and would want to keep her job.

Rose walked into the laundry room to hear Lewis asking Hughes everything about her. She realised that the staff were talking too, but she was not sure what they were saying and how much they knew. She said to Lewis, "ask me, if the gossip is about me, then it will be straight from the horse's mouth." Lewis managed to turn this against Rose saying that they were supposed to be friends, she had told Hughes everything and left her out of it. Rose replied that they were all close friends but sharing a room with Hughes made them closer and they became best friends. "I can tell Jean anything," She said. Lewis felt betrayed by the comments, "You can't call her Jean, that's not allowed," Lewis blurted. Rose asked Lewis, "what's your first name?" Lewis shot down the request firmly. "It is all right Rose. You will be leaving here soon, we are not, so don't go making trouble for us," Lewis snarled. Rose rolled her eyes, went to the table, and took the needle and thread and started sewing a pillowcase. She had a nauseous feeling as she worked, not sure what was causing it, was it because she was tired as she had not slept, over the last couple of nights. After about an hour, she said to the girls, "I am not feeling well, so I am going to my room to lie down." Lewis ignored her and left for the bathroom. Hughes replied, all right we will see you later."

Rose exited to go to her room. On the way to her bedroom, she heard raised voices in the corridor. She softly pushed the door open a little, just enough to hear what was being discussed. She saw two shadows and peered a little closer through the gap in the door and noticed it was the prince and his private secretary, Hardinge. "Sir, let us go into your office and we can discuss it there." Hardinge pleaded. The prince paced back and forth, "No, there is nothing to discuss with you. I need to go out, we can talk later," the prince ranted. Rose stepped backwards to not be seen through the gap of the door, and as the voices lowered, she continued heading towards her room.

She curled up on her bed and could not help but think what would happen to her. She turned to her side and fell asleep. Without knowing how long, she woke suddenly in a fluster and quickly headed back to the laundry room. "That was quick! Lewis has not come back from the bathroom," Hughes said. She could see that Rose was not looking well but did not know what to suggest. She explained to Rose that they were all talking about her in the kitchen, and it would not be long before they put two and two together. Rose knew she only had a couple of days left before she was leaving, and in a panic, she sent a telegram to Arthur Powell at the Maypole.

---

*My dearest Arthur,*

*I need to speak to you when I return. I will be home on the midday train on Friday. Please meet me at the station, there is something I need to tell you.*

*I am not sure what time the train from Newport will get me back into Hereford, but please wait for me.*

*Rose*

---

On the Friday of that week, Rose was getting ready to leave her post at York House. She spoke to Mr Hardinge about what they had discussed earlier in that week concerning the pregnancy. He explained that he had spoken with Mr Wigram, the King's Private Secretary, and was waiting on a response to the matter. He told Rose that she would hear from him soon. Rose began saying her goodbyes to everyone she had worked with and thanked Mrs Gray for her support and kindness towards her. Everyone wished her well as she was leaving. Lewis said goodbye to Rose and continued eating her breakfast. Hughes on the other hand, walked Rose to the door. Hughes pulled Rose in and hugged her tightly. "take care of yourself, keep in touch. If I hear anything about you, I will keep you informed and make a note in my diary." Rose was tearful as Hughes said goodbye to her dearest friend. She picked up her bag and the box with her fur coat in, and walked away from the door of York House. As she looked back, she saw Jean wave, step back inside and close the door. She was heartbroken at the thought that she was leaving her Royal position, and her best friend Jean; not knowing what was going to happen with her and the prince's baby.

Rose was in a taxi making her way to Paddington Station, she asked the driver if he could take her along Oxford Street, so she could take in the view of Selfridges along the way. On arrival she boarded the train, this brought back memories of the first time she had done so. Her thoughts recurring through her mind of where to sit, which way to travel, and where to put her luggage. She did not want to let go of the box and held it across her lap. The carriage soon began to fill, with the passing of people this convinced Rose to keep both hands pressed firmly upon the box. She had decided to sit facing forward, in the direction of travel of the train for the journey home, so she could watch the fields approaching.

# Chapter 27

# WELCOME HOME PARTY

R ose had not heard anything from Arthur, she was thinking about what she should do if he was not there for her at the station. After what seemed like a long journey home, Rose's train began pulling into the station at Hereford. Rose peered out of the window to see if she could see Arthur, but there was no sign of him. As she stood on the step of the train she looked up and down the platform. Her heart sank as she could not see him anywhere, she walked across the platform heading for the exit when a voice broke the anguish in her head. "Welcome home, I am glad you're safe," the voice said. Rose turned and saw Arthur's smiling face greeting her. She threw her arms around him and held onto him for just a few minutes. "I'm glad to be home too," she whispered, as she tightly hugged him. "Now now Rose, I didn't think you would miss me that much." Rose smiled at Arthur and said she had so much to tell him about her escapade. Arthur picked up Rose's bag and was about to take the box from her when Rose said, "I can manage this, thank you." Arthur wondered what was in the box and asked, "What's in the box?" Rose said, "you will have to wait, I will show you tomorrow. Did you mention to my mum that you were picking me up from the station?" Arthur had not spoken to her mum and was surprised that Rose had not let her parents know that she was on her way home. Rose remarked how she felt remorseful, she had only sent one letter to them, after being away for so long. They walked out of the station together, Arthur guided Rose to his horse and cart. "Not like the taxis in London," he chuckled to himself. "Come on, I will take you home." Arthur helped Rose up onto the cart, he then climbed on and drove the horse on, in the direction of home.

Arthur was looking at Rose, as they made their way out of Hereford, he could see she looked tired. Asking her if they had overworked her in London, Rose said, "I had a very nice time, I met some lovely people and I have so much news to tell you, but I need to rest first," On arrival at the Lawns Arthur got off the cart first, helping Rose down by holding her around her waist he joked, "The food must have been plentiful at the palace as you have gained a little weight." Rose looked at him with no reply. Arthur picked up Rose's bag and handed her the box, as May and James approached from the side of the house, "Evening Arthur, who is this stranger you have brought to us?" May provoked. "I didn't know you were home today Rose." Rose looked at them, "Hello dad, hello May, I thought I would surprise you." James invited Arthur into the house with Rose's bag, Rose walked in behind him. Would you like a cup of tea Arthur?" asked Elizabeth. "Yes please, look who I found at the station." Arthur stepped aside presenting Rose. Arthur realised from Elizabeth's reaction that the feeling of happiness to have Rose back was not mutual across her family. "Oh, so you have decided to come home then!" gibed Elizabeth. Rose began defending her return home, "Look, the position is finished. You and dad both said I could stay until the job was done and it is. I have not stayed any longer." Just as an argument was about to erupt, Jim came running through the door. Rose's eyes beamed with excitement at the thought of Jim missing her, but he greeted her with a plain, "Hello mum." He turned to Elizabeth and asked, "Granny can I have a drink?"

Rose leaned forward to Jim, "Jim, give me a cuddle then, I haven't seen you for a long time." Jim shook his head, "No, I'm too big for cuddles and I only cuddle granny and Aunty May." Rose scowled at Jim's response. "As you please. I will take my luggage up to my room to get it out of everyone's way. Can I have a cup of tea please mum?" Rose took her things to her room; she was upset that she did not feel welcome. In her room Rose unpacked her bag and realised she had left the box downstairs. She went back down to get the box, and as she picked it up, May queried, "What's in here then?" Rose told her it was a coat as she opened the box carefully to expose a folded full-length fur coat. She lifted it out and held it up for the room to see. They were all curious about where the coat had come from. James remarked "How could you get a coat like that!" "What! You think I would have stolen it? What do you think I am?" "Well, that's what we are all wondering. Not many people we know could afford a coat like that," May remarked. Arthur was quiet and did not engage in the conversation but had a puzzled look on his face. He told them he had to leave and take the horse home before dark. Before saying goodnight, he asked Rose if he could see her tomorrow. "Yes, call by after tea," Rose replied. Arthur left the house hearing the mumbled sounds of arguments behind the closed door. A short time later, Rose had drank two cups of tea and had a bite to eat. Elizabeth suggested they all had an early night and start the day fresh tomorrow. Rose headed to her room and collapsed on her bed; she was feeling too tired to sleep. She could hear the whispers bouncing off the walls from downstairs. Elizabeth and James were discussing the quality of the fur coat and how she came to have it.

The morning seemed to come too soon for Rose, she woke up feeling tired and drained as if she had had no sleep. The door to her room swung open. "Come on Rose, do you want to do the chicken coup or the fireplaces?" May inquired. Rose wasn't feeling in the mood to do either one that morning, and said to May, "can't they wait until I get up?" And she pulled the covers over her head. When she finally got out of bed, she washed, got dressed and went downstairs. Elizabeth was in the kitchen preparing the vegetables for lunch. "Right your ladyship, from today you will take Jim to school and help with the chores. May and I have done more than enough to help you, and now that I have your interest, I would like to ask how you came to be in possession of that fur coat." Rose looked to her mother, "If you look in the left pocket of the coat, there is a little velvet box. Open it up and maybe you will understand a little better." Elizabeth put her hand in the pocket of the fur coat and her eyes widen when she touched the velvet box. She pulled it out and opened it, "Oh my. Who on earth could afford to give you this? Are you engaged?" She questioned. Rose shook her head, "No. Not engaged, but I thought I was. I fooled myself into thinking that everything was real but sadly it's not." Elizabeth was confused by what Rose was saying, "What are you saying? You are, or are not? Someone gave you gifts like this, and you are not engaged?" Rose was looking pale and began breathing heavy. Elizabeth's inquiries moved from the gifts, and she focused on Rose not looking so well. "You look a bit pale; do you need to see the Doctor?" she asked. "It's alright mum, I know exactly what I have picked up." Elizabeth told Rose to go back upstairs and rest in bed, "I will bring you up some toast and tea." Rose lay in bed sleeping for most of the day and then woke up just before six o'clock feeling hungry, she remembered Arthur was coming around to see her. She jumped out of bed and quickly got dressed and went downstairs.

Arthur knocked on the front door, prepared to meet Rose as planned the day before. Elizabeth answered, inviting him in, Rose was drinking tea sat at the table. "Do you fancy going for a walk Rose?" Elizabeth remarked to Arthur, how Rose had been in bed all day feeling unwell. "I would love to walk with you, but I need to rest today. Can we take a walk tomorrow night Arthur?" Arthur smiled at Rose and agreed to return the following evening for their walk. With this Arthur was feeling disheartened, Elizabeth showed him to the door. She then returned to chat to Rose, "Well, it's nice to see you so keen on him, I did not think you wanted to go out with him before London, what's changed?" Rose lifted her head, looking up to her mother, "Maybe I was wrong, I think he is just what I need." Elizabeth sat down at the table with Rose, "Need, what do you mean by that?" Rose pulled her tea closer and took another sip. "Put some more sugar in it, and you might feel better?" said Elizabeth. Rose finished her drink and then quickly got up and ran outside to the toilet to be sick. Elizabeth could hear her from the kitchen window. James and May returned to the house, "What the hell is wrong with Rose? She sounds like a donkey bellowing out there," said May. Elizabeth told them that Rose must have picked up a bug in London and that she would see the Doctor the next day. James was enraged, "That is all we need, we are booked up now and cannot afford to miss any of these jobs. Can you send her somewhere else for several days?" Elizabeth assured them that everything would be all right. "May and I will be going to the far field tomorrow, to repair the fence, we will be gone all morning. Can Rose pick up Jim from school in case we don't make it back in time?" asked James. Elizabeth told him not to worry as she would make sure Jim was picked up from school.

## Chapter 28

## DON'T LIE TO ME

The next morning, Jim went to school with Rose, May and James went to the far field to work on the fence. When Rose returned, Elizabeth asked her to come and sit with her, as she needed to know what was going on with her. Rose was trying to reassure her mother that she was fine. "Rose, you are not fine. I heard you yesterday, heck, even the neighbours could hear you. The last time you were sick like that, you were pregnant with Jim. Are you pregnant Rose? Do not lie to me, I need to know." Rose began tearing up and nodded, I am about three months pregnant." Rose cried. Elizabeth turned to Rose, "Is that how you got that coat and ring, by dropping your knickers?" Rose shot down the allegations that she had sex for these gifts. "No, no, of course not. I slept with him before I got the coat and ring." Elizabeth stood up with disgust at her daughter, "Why the hell are you like this? Do you know what they call women who do this kind of thing for money and gifts? Did you go to London to be a prostitute?" Rose was crying, begging for her mother to let her explain but Elizabeth continued, "Is that what you were out there, a prostitute? You need to get out and never come back, the shame of it, the shame you have brought to this family." Elizabeth was so upset, that she was drying her eyes with her handkerchief. Rose used that opportunity to try to explain. "How could you think I would do that? Come on mother, how? I will tell you. I fell for the prince, and he bought me the fur coat and when he gave me the ring, I thought he wanted to marry me. I was in love with him, and I thought he was in love with me too."

"What do you mean the prince, what prince? Do mean the Prince of Wales? Come on, tell me the truth," Elizabeth fumed. Rose could not help but laugh with shock of her mother not believing her. "I am telling you the truth." "Fine, let's say I believe you, tell me from the beginning, how this happened?" Rose started explaining everything to her mother. How she met the prince in his room, he was sweet and kind, and they fell in love. He then bought her a fur coat as a surprise, and a few weeks later, he gave her the emerald ring. She thought he loved her as much as she loved him. She continued explaining to her mother that her David, the Prince of Wales, knew that she was carrying his baby. Rose then went on to say that she had spoken to his private secretary, Mr Hardinge, about the situation and that he was going to sort something out for her and the baby, but she did not know what. Elizabeth was upset and angry with Rose for being so foolish. "What about Arthur, where does he fit into all of this? Does he know anything at all?" Rose was shying away from the questions. "Well Rose? Does he know, are you going to tell him?" Rose looked up with shame, "I wasn't going to tell him. I was going to ask him to marry me as soon as possible. You know how keen he is around me." Elizbeth could not believe what Rose was suggesting and was becoming even more angry. "I can't believe this is how I raised you Rose, a liar and a tart, I cannot believe you are my daughter. What the hell is your father going to say?" Rose pleaded with her mum not to tell her dad until she had spoken to Arthur first. Elizabeth told Rose to stay out of her sight, go to her room. Rose went up to her room, Elizabeth sat at the table crying in despair, disappointed over her daughter's behaviour.

James and May returned home from the far field. "We are home dear, is lunch ready?" James called out. He could see Elizabeth had been crying with her tear-stained face. "What's happened, is everything alright?" He asked. Elizabeth told him she had something in her eye which was making it weep. He told her to lean her head back and he would have a look. She lifted her eyelid to show him, "can you see anything," she said, knowing there was nothing there. "No" he replied. James told her to lean her head back, and he placed a wet flannel over her eye. Moments later, Elizabeth lifted the flannel and looked at James telling him that she felt much better and rubbed his arm for his support. James took some bread and cheese off the side and asked May if she was making a pot of tea. "Where's Rose?" May asked. Elizabeth replied that Rose had gone for a walk as she was feeling a little better. Elizabeth knew that Rose wouldn't come downstairs while her father and May were there. They soon finished their lunch and were back outside working. Elizabeth called up to Rose, "come down and have some lunch." There was no response, Rose, was laid on her bed in a world of her own, feeling sorry for herself, she did not want to talk to her mother or anyone. Ten minutes later Elizabeth called up to Rose again, with anger in her voice, "Rose if you do not come down here now, I will go out and tell your father everything I know!" Rose picked herself up off the bed and made her way downstairs. As she entered the kitchen, Elizabeth looked at her, Rose looked shamefaced with her red puffy eyes from her sobbing. Elizabeth demanded that, "When Arthur Powell comes here later, you will go for a walk with him and tell him you are pregnant with the prince's baby. Beg him for marriage as this will help diminish your shame. We have a bit of money saved, tell him we will give it to him, if he marries you before you get fat, and everyone can see you're pregnant."

Later that afternoon, Rose had done her hair, and was waiting for Arthur to arrive. She put her coat on ready and was standing at the window when she saw him approaching the house. Before he could get to the door, Rose was outside to meet him. She linked her arm through his and they walked off towards Much Dewchurch. Elizabeth was looking through the window watching them leave.

# Chapter 29

# WILL YOU DO ME THE HONOUR?

As they walked on this summer's evening, Arthur and Rose chatted about the fields, cattle, and sheep on the farm. Rose found it difficult to concentrate as her thoughts were with York House, and the position she was in. Arthur could see she wasn't paying attention, "what's worrying you Rose," he asked. Rose told him she was wondering what Hughes and Lewis would be up to at that moment. "Don't worry about them, lets enjoy this warm evening walk together" he said, as he watched the birds swooping around after the insects. "I have only just got back, my head still thinks it's in London, do you want to get married Arthur?" He looked at Rose and smiled, "of course, one day, when I can afford a place of my own?" Rose turned to Arthur, "I want to get married straight away, tomorrow, or next week, what do you think?" Arthur hesitated, "steady on there, we can't get married just like that. We don't know each other well enough to do that. What's your rush?" Rose stared at him and with a big sigh, she said, "I need to get married, I have to, my mother said she can pay you, but I need to get married straight away," then she burst into tears. Arthur looked puzzled at Rose crying and pleading with him to marry her. "Why, what's going on, what aren't you telling me? Do you really need to get married that quickly? There's only one reason I can think of that you would need to marry so quick, is that why you are looking a little larger these days? Are you pregnant, is that the only reason you want to marry me?" Rose was crying more and more with every word Arthur said. "You have always looked down on me and now I'm good enough for you to marry. What the hell are you playing at?" Arthur stormed off, leaving Rose to make her own way home.

Rose arrived home, sniffling and feeling sorrier for herself. She walked in and Elizabeth, May, James, and Jim were talking. "Did you enjoy your walk?" James asked. Rose was rubbing her face, "No, not today, Arthur walked off in a sulk, you know what he's like." Elizabeth glared at her, as Rose went up to her room for a lie down. Rose could hear James and May talking about her as she was walking upstairs. "Well, it must be serious between them if they can row about it," James wondered. "About what?" Elizabeth replied. "Well, anything, it doesn't take a lot. I remember us when we had our first row, when we were courting. If I hadn't been in love with you, we would not be here now. Elizabeth was shocked by James's remark. "Would we not indeed! No one else would have you," Elizabeth said. As she leaned over and kissed James on the head. Elizabeth left the room and went up to see Rose, to find out what her and Arthur had argued over.

Rose began telling her mother all about Arthur, what was said, and how he reacted when he felt Rose was using him to get out of her situation. "What am I to do? I have one child and another on the way and no husband," Rose said in desperation. "I thought you said the prince was going to help you?" queried Elizabeth. With tears running down her cheeks and placing her head into her mother's lap, Rose said to her mum, "I don't know what to do." Elizabeth said, "you must get up, and stop crying, it will not help anything. "If he got you pregnant, then he will have to pay. Are you sure it was the prince and no one else?" Elizabeth asked. Rose looked annoyed at her mother's question. "Yes, it was the prince and no one else. Why can't you understand that?" Elizabeth thought to herself, how they would need to deal with the situation, a prince has got her daughter pregnant, and must deal with his wrongdoing. "Right, then we shall have to send a letter to him and see what he says." Rose told her mother not to do that, "I have already spoken to his Private Secretary Mr Hardinge. He said he would sort it out, they say he is an honest man and true to his word, and I will wait to hear from him." Elizabeth was not as sure as Rose that she would receive anything from the prince or his private secretary.

# Chapter 30

# IN IT FOR THE MONEY

A few days had passed since Arthur had fallen out with Rose; all she had thought about was how they had argued. On top of this she was also worrying that she still had not received anything from Mr Hardinge back in London. Arthur turned up at the house, knocking on the door, Rose opened it and was surprised to see him standing there. She jeered at Arthur asking if he was going to call her names or make her feel bad again. Arthur said he had been thinking and asked if they could talk about a solution to her problem. Rose grabbed her coat and they walked off up the lane. In the house, James remarked to Elizabeth, "there's nothing to worry about, now the squabbling is over they will make up and get back together." Elizabeth raised her eyebrows and nodded.

"So, Arthur, why are you really here?" Rose asked. Arthur continued walking with Rose, thinking of how he would explain, and then replied, "Well, I have thought about it, and have decided it might be worth it for both of us, getting together. I can have a deposit for a farm, and you can have a husband and the Royal Bastard will have a father." Rose slapped Arthur across the face. "So, you came back here for the money and only the money, my parents worked hard all their lives and you are willing to take it, and you think I have no shame!" Arthur put his face closer to Rose and raging said, "You can please yourself, but what you need is a husband and pretty quick by the look of you, and I want a down-payment for a farm of my own. Think how much you would get for that fur coat and that ring." Rose cringed at Arthur's words, "I will not be selling that coat or anything else to pay you Arthur Powell. Nothing at all." "Well, you were the one in the first place to mention your mother's money; and, how else are you going to get a husband if you do not pay someone? I do not think anyone around here will marry you carrying someone else's bastard child, you will be the talk of the town, bring shame on your parents." Rose's baby belly was beginning to show, and she had no idea what to do. Rumours were already beginning to spread about her pregnancy, and that it was Arthurs, as he was the only male she had been seen stepping out with. Even Arthurs own family thought he was the father, but he would not confirm or deny it when asked. Rose agreed that Arthur was right about what he said. She said, "Arthur if this is what it takes then we have an understanding." Rose and Arthur returned home, and Rose was feeling more settled as she went back into the house.

Some time had passed, Arthur went to Rose with a plan for them to go to London. They would speak to the prince about what he was going to do about the baby. Rose was now looking quite big and was glowing with motherhood. James came into the kitchen, he asked Arthur when he was going to marry Rose. "As soon as I have the time, I want to get married before the baby arrives you know." Elizabeth said, "I will speak to the vicar about a time and date, as we cannot leave things much longer." Arthur left the house, still thinking of going to London to speak to the prince.

He stuck to his plan of taking Rose to London when she was heavily pregnant to confront the prince. At this point, in October 1933, Rose was now eight months pregnant. Arthur told her of his plans. They were to catch a train and go back to London, shaming the prince for what he had done and now he had to pay for it. Arthur had saved the train fare, knowing Rose would do as she was told if she wanted him to marry her. Rose was not happy about Arthur's conniving plan, she was feeling uncomfortable at home, the last thing she wanted was a long train journey. Rose told her mother and father that Arthur was taking her out for the day, and not what Arthur had planned, as they would have stopped them. Arthur arranged for his brother Frank to take them to the station. He and Rose caught the early morning train to Newport, they then sat on the platform and waited for the connecting train to London. Rose was in pain and wanted to return home, but Arthur was having none of it. "We are on the way now; you will be fine." The London train pulled into the station; Arthur helped Rose up into the carriage and showed her to a seat.

When they arrived in London, Rose wanted to get a taxi, but Arthur insisted they walked as he did not have much money left. He pulled Rose by the arm through the streets of London until they reached York House. As they did not have an appointment, they waited outside hoping someone that Rose knew would come out of the house. Rose looked to see if Samual, Hughes's love interest was on duty, but he was not. After a brief time of sitting on a bench, Rose spotted Page, and called out to her. She approached with a warm welcoming smile to Rose. "I need to see Mr Hardinge, is he here?" asked Rose.

Page took Rose and Arthur into the house and took them to the kitchen; she then went to find Mrs Gray. When Mrs Gray arrived, she looked at Arthur and was not pleased with the first impression he gave, he was cocky and arrogant. He was the one that was demanding to see Mr Hardinge. Mr Williams came into the kitchen wanting to know what the commotion was about. Mrs Gray explained that Rose and the young man were there to see Mr Hardinge, but they had no appointment. Mr Williams said he would find out if Mr Hardinge was available. Rose became extremely uncomfortable, and Mrs Gray could see this. She opened the door and put her arm around Rose to take her into the other room. As Rose moved, Arthur grabbed her arm, saying, "where are you going!" Mrs Gray pushed his hand off Rose, and told him that she was going with her, and he needed to stay where he was. She took Rose into her room and sat her into a large soft chair and offered her some tea to drink. Arthur did not argue as he was wanting to speak to Mr Hardinge, he then sat down in the kitchen waiting for Mr Williams to return. Twenty minutes later Mr Williams with Mr Hardinge following entered the kitchen. Looking at Arthur, and the way he was dressed, in his oversized jacket, Mr Hardinge was weighing Arthur up. "Where is Rose?" He asked. Arthur told him that Rose had gone with "that woman to rest in her room," and pointed in the direction of Mrs Gray's room. Mr Hardinge huffed and got Mr Williams to accompany him to Mrs Gray's room, leaving Arthur in the kitchen with the Cook, who was busy preparing lunch.

Mr Hardinge knocked on the door of the room and Mrs Gray opened it. Rose was not looking well, being heavily pregnant, every now and again she would let out a wince of pain. Mr Hardinge was not impressed with Rose turning up without an appointment, as it was not the right thing to do, he asked her why she was there. "I'm due to have this baby sir." He then asked Mrs Gray and Mr Williams to give them some privacy in the room. At one point, Rose thought he had forgotten who she was until she mentioned the baby, he then changed his attitude towards her. "I would like Arthur to join me please sir." Mr Hardinge opened the door to Mr Williams who was standing outside. "Go and get the boy," he said. Within a couple of minutes, Arthur joined them. "What is it you want?" he asked Arthur. "Well. I will marry Rose and take the kid off your hands, but we need money to bring him up as my own." Mr Hardinge looked stunned at Arthur's approach and before he could reply, Rose let out a big scream of pain. Arthur took hold of Rose's hand, "What's wrong?" he asked. "I think the baby is coming." Mr Hardinge called for Mrs Gray. She came rushing in. "Get her out of here!" Mr Hardinge ordered. "It cannot be born here! Move her somewhere else!" Mr Hardinge left the room. She could see that Rose could not be moved so she called for the doctor. She turned to Mr Williams and Arthur and told them to go to the kitchen, and to send the cook to her room.

Mrs Gray and the cook helped Rose get ready for the birth, talking to her to calm her. "Well Rose, I am not sure what to do as I have never had any children." Mrs Gray turned to the cook, "Any ideas?" The cook shook her head and told her that she had seen the dog have puppies once and she got on with it herself. Mrs Gray shook her head in disbelief that the cook would think that a dog and a human birth could be considered the same. Rose began pushing and then stopped. Mrs Gray asked cook to fetch some towels and hot water. The contractions went on for hours and then, "the baby is coming. I can't stop it," Rose screamed.

# Chapter 31

# A ROYAL BABY

The baby was born on the floor of Mrs Gray's room. She washed the new-born baby boy and wrapped him in a large white towel, and then helped Rose wash as she sat in the armchair. By this time, there was a commotion in the corridor outside. The staff had heard the noise of Rose giving birth and Mr Williams was trying to send them all away. They then had a visit from Mr Wigram who wanted to know what had happened. He was with Mr Hardinge who was panicking, not knowing how to handle the situation, whereas Mr Wigram was calm, not a lot phased him. He asked if he could speak to Rose. Mrs Gray was worried about Rose and the baby. She thought he looked quite small, having not seen a new-born baby before. The doctor had informed Mrs Gray that both Rose and the baby were fine but should not be moved until the following day as she needed rest. Mr Wigram went into the room. He spoke to Rose in a calm manner and looked at the baby in the towel. Rose looked at Mr Wigram with relief in her face, she was feeling tired, and said, "I am sorry sir, so sorry." He could see she was upset. "That is alright Rose, just rest." Before he could continue talking to Rose, Arthur came barging into the room. "I'm just about to talk with Rose if you don't mind," Mr Wigram told Arthur. "I do mind, anyway, what's it got to do with you? The other chap was going to speak to us." This shocked Mr Wigram, "Well, the other chap, as you put it, is not dealing with the situation, I am. So, if you do not mind. ..." he held the door open for Arthur to leave. Just as Arthur was about to leave the room, Rose interrupted, "Sir, this is Arthur." Mr Wigram looked at Rose and she could see that he did not know who Arthur was. "He's my intended, he said he would marry me," Rose explained. Arthur pushed back past Mr Wigram, "That's right. I will take on the kid as soon as we sort out a deal," Arthur asserted. Mr Wigram asked Arthur in a calm manner if he could leave the room just for a moment so he could speak with Rose. Rose told Arthur to leave and assured him that everything would be all right. Mr Wigram asked Mr Williams and Mrs Gray, who were stood in the corridor, if they could take Arthur to the kitchen for a cup of tea. Mr Wigram seemed a little nervous of Rose and the baby. "Well, we have never had a situation of this kind Rose, but there are several options." Rose looked at him a little confused and asked what he meant by that. Mr Wigram continued to explain, "Well, we could find this little chap a home, and I am sure we would sort out a payment for your inconvenience, then you could marry your young man as if nothing had happened. Rose could see the sincerity in Mr Wigram's face and that he was really trying to help. She looked at the baby, she had just gave birth, "how could I give Edward away sir?" she smiled. "Oh, you have already named him," He replied. Rose continued, "Sir, I can't imagine what you must think of me. What kind of girl I am, but let me tell you, I loved his father, the Prince of Wales, and I still do! If he knows the baby is born and especially as he is born in his own home, he might change his mind and want me and his baby boy. Would it be possible to tell him I am here please sir?" Mr Wigram then realised that he read the situation wrong, and Rose did not know how the Prince of Wales was as a person. He was not most agreeable to Rose's proposal. Rose told Mr Wigram of their affair and how he had bought her gifts, including a ring. She continued telling

Mr Wigram how she believed deep down he loved her as much as she loved him. The situation seemed to be becoming more and more complicated. Mr Wigram did not know what to do at this point. He told Rose he would be back soon and that she should rest.

He headed off towards Mr Hardinge's office. Mrs Gray went to keep Rose and the baby company. She asked, "have you given him a name?" "Yes," Rose replied. "His name is Edward Albert." Mrs Gray moved back slightly. "Do you think that's wise?" Rose defended her decision. "I can't imagine what everyone thinks of me, but I really loved his father, and I am sure he loved me." Mrs Gray touched Rose's hand, "What will you do now my girl?" "Well Arthur wants to marry me," she replied. Mrs Gray flustered at the thought, "are you sure he's the right person for you to marry? He appears to look out for himself more than you," she remarked. Mr Wigram came back to the room and knocked on the door. This interrupted the conversation between Mrs Grey and Rose. He asked Mrs Gray if she could go to Selfridges and buy clothes for the baby, and to also make sure Rose had a change of clothing for her journey home. Mrs Gray was only too pleased as she had never shopped for baby clothes before. She left to find Rose a change of dress, as she could have hers laundered. Mr Wigram asked if Rose was up to discussing the future of the baby and she agreed. He told her he had spoken to the Palace and also that payments were to be made for the child's wellbeing. He did not know exactly how much at this point or when Rose would receive the money. She was asked to keep everything quiet at this time and to have no further contact of any kind with the Prince of Wales. He explained to Rose that he would contact her, asking for her address and her bank account. She said, "I don't have a bank account, and neither does my father, cash will be all right."

A while later, Mrs Gray returned with the dress for Rose. Mr Wigram left as Mrs Grey helped her to change. "I will take a taxi up to Selfridges and pick up some clothes for Edward," she said. Arthur came in to sit with Rose, Mrs Gray told Arthur that Rose must rest and if they needed anything, he was to go to the Kitchen and cook would help him. An hour and a half later Mrs Grey returned loaded up with; towelling nappies, three dresses with matching bonnets, two white cardigans, and a white cotton shawl; for Rose she had a new dress. Edward was then dressed in a dress with lace on it and a matching bonnet. The dress Mrs Gray had bought for Rose was a little big but as she explained, "you would not want anything tight on the train journey home, as it would be uncomfortable". That night Arthur was sent to a room in the male servant quarters. Rose spent the night in a room close to Mrs Gray.

The next morning Rose was dressed, and Edward was fed and changed, then wrapped in his shawl. Mr Wigram was with Rose in the sitting room, he gave her an envelope and asked her to put it into her handbag, not to open it until she was safely home. Arthur was asked to come from the kitchen into the sitting room. Arthur saw Mr Wigram give Rose a full ten pounds for their journey home. This was for the taxi fare to the station and first-class tickets home. As soon as Mr Wigram left the room, Arthur held his hand out and asked Rose for the money, he would look after the money side of things from now on. Rose was too weak to argue and gave Arthur the ten pounds. As soon as they were outside York House, on their way home, Arthur said to Rose, "we will walk to the station, and save the money." Rose begged for a taxi, but Arthur began walking so she hailed a taxi herself. Arthur turned around and began to moan at Rose, but she told him that he would pay for the taxi fare, or she will go back in and tell Mr Wigram.

After some protest Arthur got into the taxi with Rose and the baby, Rose asked the taxi driver to take them to Paddington station. As they made their way to the station Arthur asked Rose, "what did Mr Wigram say to you this morning?" Rose asked Arthur to be quiet as she could sense the taxi driver was observing them. Arthur was loaded up with the things Mrs Gray had bought the baby. There were a few changes of clothes, one dozen nappies which were tied with a blue ribbon, a silver and mother of pearl rattle, still boxed. Rose wore her own jacket over the top of her new dress, and she felt happy that things were moving in the right direction. At the station, Rose reminded Arthur that they had the fare to pay for first-class tickets, but Arthur would not pay for them as they already had return tickets.

The train they travelled on was quite empty and they had a carriage to themselves. "Well Arthur, how are we going to explain this to mum and dad when we get home?" "Never mind that Rose, what happened behind the closed doors?" Rose told him everything that Mr Wigram had said. "Well, that's no good. I want to know how much and when. I mean, if I am going to marry you, I want to know how much money I am going to get, how much is it worth." Rose looked at Arthur with a cold look, "Of course Arthur. The other offer was to give Edward to Mr Wigram, and he would find him another home and then I would not need to marry you at all." At this point Arthur realised he could not push Rose too far as he wanted the money, for the deposit for a farm. Rose told Arthur to wait and see what they offered, "we have to get home first. What are you going to say as to why we went to London in the first place?" "I don't know," Arthur replied. "You will think of something" he said to Rose. "Just don't tell them about the money." Rose was annoyed at Arthur's response, "I was talking about how we are going to explain what we have for the baby and why he was born in London." Arthur hardly spoke to Rose for the rest of the journey. Rose was feeling hungry and tired, and asked Arthur who would be meeting them when they arrived in at Hereford station. "I don't know, I think we will have to walk home." During the journey, the baby felt like it was getting heavier for Rose to hold and so she asked Arthur if he could hold him while she had a little sleep. He said he could not, as he did not know how to hold a baby, anyway he had to rest. She placed baby Edward on the inside of the seat next to her, she sat on the outside, holding her arm over him so he would not fall off. She was in a light sleep and kept waking at every movement Edward made. She looked over and there was Arthur fast asleep. She knew marrying him would be wrong but to her she had no other choice. Edward slept for most of the ride on the train from London to Newport, from Newport to Hereford, Rose had to feed and change him.

Arthur woke up just before the train they were on from Newport reached Hereford station. He glanced through the window at the platform as the train rolled into the station. It was getting dark, he saw Rose's reflection holding the baby, he turned to look at her whilst yawning, he then gave her a smile. Rose did not smile back. He could tell she was not happy, although he could not understand why. Arthur stood up and began walking towards the train door when Rose asked him to help carry the bags or carry the baby. He picked up one of the bags, leaving Rose to carry the baby and the other bag. Rose was carefully walking towards the door, not wanting to get the bag caught or disturb Edward. As they got off the train, Rose was praying someone would be there to greet them and take them home, as she could hardly put one foot in front of the other, with the exhaustion she was feeling from the long Journey home.

As they crossed the platform Arthur grumbled, "Come on, get a move on Rose!" Rose was feeling in so much pain, she wanted to stop and rest. With tears falling down her face, she cried, "I can't, I can't walk all that way, I'm so tired." Arthur wanted to get home just as much as Rose did, he did not want to spend any more of his money to help get them home, even though it was getting dark. Rose was wincing every time she put a foot down on the floor from the pain she was feeling. On their walk home, the Vicar and his wife stopped to say hello to Rose and Arthur and met the baby for the first time. They could see how distraught Rose was. She begged them to give her a lift home, but they were heading in the opposite direction to see a parishioner. Rose told them how she had just given birth to the baby the day before and how tired she was. Arthur had continued walking ahead. The Vicar could see that Arthur was not interested in helping Rose, he got out of the car and put Rose and the baby into the back of it. The Vicar turned the car around to take Rose home, the Vicar's wife chatted with Rose about the baby and how lovely he looked in his shawl. "I went to London with Arthur yesterday and gave birth there, he is early, but the Doctor said he would be all right. Arthur and I came home but Arthur did not call anyone to pick us up from the station." The Vicar's wife gasped at what Rose was saying, as they were driving down the road. They then saw Arthur walking alone along the road in front of them, the Vicar's wife said to her husband, "don't stop as I believe Arthur wanted to walk home." they continued driving past Arthur, leaving him to walk home alone.

They drove Rose to the Lawns chatting along the way. Her parents Elizabeth and James greeted them with confusion as to why the Vicar and his wife were bringing Rose home, then they saw Rose cradling something in her arms. The Vicar explained the situation, how they saw Rose walking along the road with Arthur ahead, making their way home. Elizabeth took baby Edward from Rose as she looked like she was going to collapse from exhaustion. Rose said to her mother this is Edward, she explained how he was born the day before, that everything was fine with him, and that the doctor had checked him over. Elizabeth looked at Edward and noticed he did not have any fingernails or eye lashes – he was all there but was not fully formed due to the early birth. She asked, "where's Arthur?" Rose explained how he wanted to walk home so she had not seen him since they passed him in the car. The Vicar then said, "we must go now as we are late for a meeting," and as they drove off, all three thanked them for driving Rose and Edward home. Elizabeth noticed how well Edward was dressed, she asked Rose, "these are fancy clothes, where did you get them?" Rose said Arthur got them for him. James put the bags down in the house as Elizabeth held Edward in her arms. "I will be having words with Arthur, he needs to marry Rose now," James ranted. A short time later Arthur turned up at the house with Roses other bag. He said to Elizabeth that he did not mind walking as he was used to it from a young lad. He gave the bag to her and said he would call by tomorrow and said his good nights. Arthur's parents were not in agreement to the marriage proposal, as they had their doubts about the baby being Arthurs. He had never told them the truth about the baby's real father and planned to marry Rose anyway. During the night, Rose woke up four times to feed baby Edward, Elizabeth had a restless night too, deep in thought, she listened out for any sign that Rose needed help.

In the morning Elizabeth opened the door, Rose was fast asleep, and as she looked by the side of the bed, she could see baby Edward asleep in the drawer. She left them to rest and went downstairs. May was in the kitchen eating her breakfast, she said, "I have taken Jim to school, and I will collect him later," she knew Rose would be preoccupied for a while. May asked Elizabeth who she thought the father was, as she believed it was not Arthurs. "Right, we will have less of that, if anyone asks, Arthur is the father, do you understand," Elizabeth growled. From this May believed that Arthur was not the real father but agreed to mask the truth.

Around ten o'clock, Arthur called by to check on Rose and baby Edward. Elizabeth greeted Arthur at the door, "is everything all right with you and Rose? Rose told me everything." Arthur seemed surprised that Rose would have told her family everything, unaware to how much they knew, he responded, "It will all turn out all right, I am sure. You know about our arrangement, I will marry Rose this afternoon, and take on the kid as my own, for the fact they will pay us money to look after him, I can get the farm I wanted to buy." Arthur then knew that Rose did not tell them the whole story, by the expression on Elizabeth's face. "She didn't explain all of that to me," Elizabeth replied. Arthur shrugged it off and said that it must have slipped her mind. Elizabeth then said to him, "You know you both have to be at the church by 3pm today." The Vicar will not be impressed with you if you are late. Arthur left, as he had a lot to do before that afternoon. Their wedding took place Wednesday 18th October as Arthur and Rose agreed, only two days after Edwards birth date.

# Chapter 32

# MIDDLE MILL FARM

A rthur managed to put his down-payment on a small farm called, Middle Mill Farm. It was cold and damp and they had no furniture to move into the farm with. Rose's parents gave them a couple of chairs. They got an old kitchen table from the Maypole which had a wonky leg. They also managed to get a horsehair mattress, so they had something to sleep on. Rose had packed all her clothes from the Lawns. "I've done this before," she said to May. "How long do you think it will last?" May asked. Rose looked at her with despair in her face, "why would you say something like that." May then mentioned that "you don't seem very happy together, Arthur is happier about the farm than being married to you." May also said that she believed the baby was not Arthur's. Rose did not want to talk about Edward, she quickly grabbed more clothes from the chest of drawers, threw them into the suitcase and rushed downstairs. Arthur picked her up and they left for the Mill.

On their first night's stay at Middle Mill Farm, Rose put down a blanket on top of the mattress, for her and Edward to sleep on, with no pillows to hand she used a couple of rugs to keep them warm. Arthur said he would sleep by the fire downstairs. Even with the extra blanket and rugs that Rose had put on the mattress, she found it cold and uncomfortable, but snuggled baby Edward to keep him warm.

The next morning, Rose was woken by Arthur's movements downstairs. With the house not furnished, everything echoed through the whole house. She went down to see what he was doing. "I'm going to make my house more comfortable," Arthur explained. Rose snapped back, "Your house! Don't you mean our house! Remember whose money is paying for our house, it's definitely not you." Arthur became angry and reminded Rose that without him, everyone would know what she was, especially with the baby not being his. "So, I would be quiet if I were you, it is my house he told her. What money have you got left from the palace? I saw you stash some away," he said through gritted teeth. Rose was just as angry but did not want to wake Edward, she quietly raged, "That's for food and some furniture, not for you!" Arthur got closer to Rose's face to intimidate her, saying that he wanted the money to buy a cow, to get his herd started, he demanded that she handed it over. Rose stood her ground reiterating how the money was for food and furniture. If there was any money left over, he could buy a cow but, if there was not enough, he would have to wait until the next payment came in. Arthur moved back with a slight smile that changed his whole demeanour. "Next payment. When will that be?" he gently asked. Rose told him she did not know exactly when that would be, but there were to be more payments soon. Arthur then realised that Rose must have discussed this with Mr Wigram in London when he was told to leave the room. With this Arthur became less invasive towards Rose, knowing that more money would be coming soon.

In Hereford, there was a shop that sold second-hand furniture and other household items, Rose wanted to go to buy some pieces of furniture for the house. She asked her father if they could borrow the horse and cart to get there. Rose bought, a bed frame, a dresser, pans, and spoons, a couple of metal buckets and a broom. She could not wait to get it all home. Arthur became more involved and asked his brothers to help move the furniture into the house. They took the old metal-sprung bed frame upstairs and fixed the headboard and baseboard, so the bed was solid enough to put the mattress on. The mattress did not fit properly. It was a little shorter and not wide enough, but much better than having the mattress on the floor. The large dresser was moved into the small sitting room, and when the drawers were placed in it, Rose pulled the bottom drawer open and put a blanket in to it, she placed the baby down inside for a sleep. She helped move the chairs until she felt they were in the right place close to the fire. Rose was feeling happier now that she was making it her home. She lit the fire and gave Arthur and his brothers a chunk of bread and some cheese that she had bought that morning. One of Arthur's brothers, Frank, asked him where he got the down-payment for the property and all the furniture they just bought. "Never you mind where I got the money from, I will be getting plenty more as time goes on, don't you worry," Arthur gloated. Frank looked bewildered, "Not doing anything dodgy are you, Arthur?" Arthur told him that it was not anything dodgy and joked that he found himself a small cash cow. Rose overheard what Arthur was saying to his brothers and did not want to cause a scene by confronting him there and then, she decided to wait until they left before speaking to him.

Later that day, Arthur and Rose sat in their chairs near the fireplace. Rose turned to Arthur and asked him to stop telling people, about him coming into money. She said, he will be questioned about the money, and he will have to lie about where it came from. Arthur leapt out of his chair and towered over Rose as she was sitting in hers. "Just remember what you are. A tart with a bastard kid, I only married you for money and nothing more." Rose pushed Arthur back and stood up to confront him, "Well, if that's what you think, I will give

Edward to Mr Wigram, and he can find him a new home. That will stop you." Arthur knew that although he wanted to be in control of everything, Rose was just as powerful. "You can't give the kid away; we have this place now. What would your family think? And remember, the kid isn't registered as mine yet. He's not going to be called Edward anymore," Arthur told Rose. She replied to him, "that's what it says on his birth certificate, and you can't change that." "Yes I can," Arthur responded. "You will register him in January in Hereford. We don't have to tell anyone. You can call him Royal Albert so people can know where he comes from. They can also know that I took pity on you and married you." Rose looked at Arthur with disgust at his comments, "I really think Edward would be better elsewhere and not with you Arthur," Rose hollered. Arthur could tell he had pushed Rose too far and it would be best to go out and let her calm down.

# Chapter 33

# TIMES ARE TOUGH

Arthur had difficulty in showing any emotion towards Rose now she had her new baby boy. He had waited for them to be together, but she came back from London, with the only reason to marry, pregnant with another man's child, not just any man but a Prince. Rose already had one, Jim, he was not Arthur's either. At this point, Arthur thought he made the wrong decision by agreeing to marry Rose, even if it was for money. Arthur was out all afternoon; it was beginning to get dark. Rose had made a stew and it was cooking on the fire. She lit the lamps and the house felt warm and cosy. Jim was running around the house and told to be quiet, so he did not wake up Edward, who was fast asleep. Rose heard the backdoor open and Arthur walked in. She did not know what mood he was going to be in. "We have plenty of rabbits in the far field, I will try and catch some for you tomorrow if you'd like?" He said. Rose was surprised, he seemed quite like the old Arthur she had met in the market. Rose answered him with "that's a good idea, we could do with some fresh meat." She then went on to suggest that when the weather improves, they should dig over an area of garden ready to plant vegetables in the spring. They had several orchards, mostly cider apples with some eating apples, and some cooking apples. Arthur then said, "we have plenty of apples to store and sell, they last the whole year." "Do you think we will be here in another year, Arthur? Because as things are now, I am thinking of going back to the Lawns and telling them everything," Rose taunted. Arthur took Rose's hand, "I think we had better give it a try for now and see how things go." As the late night approached, Rose said to Arthur she was feeling tired and going up to bed. She asked him to bring up the bottom drawer for Edward to sleep in. Rose then headed upstairs guiding her way with the candle in one hand, and with Edward secure in her other arm. Arthur followed behind with the bottom drawer from the dresser, he placed it at the side of the bed. Rose then gently placed Edward in the drawer and wrapped him up tightly to stay warm. "Are you coming to bed?" She whispered to Arthur. "Not right now, I will be up later," he replied. As Arthur went back downstairs, Rose undressed and climbed into bed. The mattress felt different to the night before, it was now on a bed frame, and this allowed Rose to sink into it with comfort. She began thinking of fabrics that would look good as curtains for the room, with matching covers for the bed. Her thoughts took her to the Palace and York House, how it would be lovely to have had a four-poster bed with a canopy. Rose would have loved to have had such a glamourous bedroom, but realised that matching curtains and a bed cover, would be the closest she would get to that for now. The money they were given for Edward was going quicker than it would arrive. Rose enjoyed spending it to buy things she needed for the house but had to be careful how much she spent.

As the winter months passed, Rose and Arthur found it very difficult to survive. Although Arthur was helping his brothers, and James, money was short. Arthur decided he would contact Mr Wigram at the Palace without telling Rose. He sent a telegram and in return, Mr Wigram replied that he would send someone down to see them. A few days later a man from the Palace arrived at the Mill to speak to them.

This surprised Rose to see an official from the Palace. He explained that Arthur had made contact stating they were in desperate need of money to feed the child. Arthur came home to find a man sitting at the table talking to Rose. "Good morning," Arthur said. "Good Morning," he replied, "I have come from London to check on Edward's welfare." He was there to report back to Mr Wigram. The offer was still there to find Edward a new home. Rose and Arthur were told that Mr Wigram was working on behalf of Their Majesties, they were concerned about the welfare of the boy. More money was sent for Edward on the condition that no further contact with the Palace was made. They were told that everything that was arranged and put in place up until then was it, and they would receive nothing else going forward. Rose was fuming but knew she had to keep calm until the Palace official had left. She turned to Arthur and yelled at him. She told him that under no circumstances was he to spend the money they had just received as he wished, and if he didn't like it, he could leave. Arthur began raging, calling Rose awful names, and started to call Edward a Royal bastard child again. Rose picked up the tea caddy and hurled it at him, just missing his head. She screamed she had had enough of him, and for him to get out, so he left.

The next few days were difficult; Rose was feeling depressed. Her mother and sister called by to see her, they could see she was not coping well. May was worried for Rose, but her mother was not sympathetic towards her. "The thing is Rose, you made your bed and now you must lie in it, running back home to me and your father is not the answer." Rose sat with them for about an hour as Jim ran around making lots of noise. He rushed over to May and threw his arms around her, "I miss you," he said as he kissed her on the cheek. May hugged him and then asked if he wanted to play outside, making mudpies. Rose was talking calmly to her mother, with May and Jim outside playing. Elizabeth said to Rose, "Edward is almost three months now, you need to register his birth." Rose replied, "Arthur want's to name him Royal Albert so everyone would know who he was." Elizabeth shot down that idea, "Don't be silly. He cannot be called that, keep his name as Edward Albert." Rose moved over to the drawer, which Arthur had carried back downstairs, she looked at Edward sleeping. "I want to keep his name as Edward but if I do, I know Arthur will be mean to me." This concerned Elizabeth, "has he hit you," she asked. Rose told her that, "it is worse than that, he calls me names and Edward the Royal bastard child." And she carried on to how he went behind her back to get more money from the Royal Family. "I'm ashamed, mum, ashamed of being with him but what can I do? I arranged everything with Mr Wigram and now he is trying to ruin it through his greed." Elizabeth asked Rose what Mr Wigram was like as a person. Rose told her she had only met him twice and he had been so kind and generous on both occasions. She then mentioned to Rose how worried she was about James finding out about Edwards real father, "I can't tell your father to have a word with him, otherwise he will know everything. I don't know how he would react. I hate keeping secrets from him and you know that. May is trying to work things out, she keeps asking questions. You know she likes her chats with Arthur, you need to make sure he does not tell her anything."

# Chapter 34

# THE BOY WITH TWO NAMES

It was later January when Rose decided it was time to register Edward. She told Arthur she was going into town and that he was to keep an eye on the boys. Rose managed to get a lift in with the neighbour and went straight to the Registry Office. She registered baby Edward as Roy Albert Powell, hoping this would make Arthur a little happier. She did not want to name him Royal Albert as she was worried this would be questioned and could expose his true identity. Rose smiled and said thank you to the registrar, placed the birth certificate in her bag before she made her way home. She did not see anyone she knew and missed the only bus that went on the route home. It took a while to get home, but as Rose journeyed, she imagined that things were going to be better from now on.

Arriving home Rose heard screams from within the house, she rushed in to find Jim soaking wet, he had fallen into the water, Roy Albert was on his side in the drawer screaming. Rose quickly picked up Roy Albert and cradled him to comfort him. "Where is Arthur!" She asked Jim. "He's outside in the shed," Jim replied. Rose asked him how he got wet, and Jim told her, he was playing by the house and fell in the water. She pulled Jim close to her waist and held him tight in disbelief that Arthur had left them both alone. She quickly sat down as her legs began wobbling from the fear and a reminder of how her first husband, Fred, had drowned in the brook. She sat there cradling both her children for a few minutes.

Raging, Rose then went outside to Arthur in the shed. "You were supposed to be looking after the children! You could not even do that. You are nothing but a fool, an idiot, I hate you! I wish you would die in the water, and I would not be in this mess!" she yelled at Arthur as she was beating at his chest. Arthur was dumfounded, "What the hell is wrong with you, you mad woman?" He questioned. "What's wrong with me, it's not me, it's you! Jim nearly drowned in the mill water and the baby was screaming in the draw," she blurted. Arthur looked at Jim, "Now tell your mother what really happened, The truth." Rose stopped raging just to hear what Jim had to say. "The bucket fell on me," confessed Jim. Arthur continued explaining what happened, "The bucket was in the sink, full of cold water with scraps and peelings and Jim picked it up and by the time he got to the backdoor, he was trailing water behind him and slipped, pouring it all down himself. I came to the shed to get the bath to give him a wash. I told Jim to watch the baby while I got it." Rose walked over to Jim with her hand raised to hit him as he cowered away. She slapped him with her left hand as she held Roy in her right arm. Rose intended to send Jim to bed, but Arthur said, "he needs a bath to get the scraps off him and the smell." Rose could see that Arthur was serious and concerned about Jim, so they made their way indoors. She passed Roy Albert to Arthur and asked him to sit in the chair out of the way. She began to pour water into the bath, as she did, Jim stripped off his clothes and headed for the bath. Arthur quickly grabbed Jim's arm to stop him from going straight into the boiling water. "You can't go straight in. It needs cold water first or you will burn yourself." Rose got a pale of cold water from the kitchen tap and pored it into the tin bath. Jim jumped in splashing in the six inches of water. Rose began undressing Roy Albert and told Arthur she will give him a bath too as the water was there. As she was bathing Roy, she said to Arthur, "I have registered baby Edward, and he will now be known as Roy Albert Powell, No Royal, just Roy, if I am honest, I would have liked to have kept it as Edward. I know you wanted to name him Royal but that was never going to work and so he has been registered as Roy and that is final." Arthur looked at Rose, "Roy is close enough to Royal." Rose was surprised that Arthur was so understanding with the babies new name.

It took a few days for the family to get used to calling Edward, Roy. Rose thought that changing his name was a good way for her to try forgetting the prince. She thought she was in control of her feelings towards David, wanting to not love him as she had once before; knowing he never loved her, but when she looked at Roy, she could see he looked so much like his father the Prince of Wales. Rose found it difficult living at the farm, with an outside toilet, and only one tap in the kitchen that produced cold water. She missed the inside toilet and bathroom she had become accustomed to in London and found it hard to stomach anything else. Over the following months, she became closer to Arthur, he was becoming more reasonable. The weather was better, the sun made them all more cheerful from being outside. The orchard trees were full of blossom, and it looked like it would be a good crop this season. Arthur was planning to sell the apples to the local cider factory, Bulmers in Hereford. Although things were looking up, Rose was still feeling lonely and empty at times. This was the lifestyle Arthur wanted, but Rose wanted different, not a farmer's wife. She began to resent the mischief Jim was causing. The lies he was telling between him and Arthur. Rose could tell he did not like Arthur and that Arthur disliked him too, so it was the bickering from time to time that drove Rose crazy. Roy was crawling around everywhere and growing, Rose had to make him new clothes. He was now too big for the drawer, so Arthur made a cot for him to sleep in. Arthur used reused and new wooden pieces to make it twice as long as the drawer of the dresser and added some high sides. They put the new cot in Jim's room, Jim protested, he did not want to share his room with his baby brother. He kept asking to live with his grandparents and May at the Lawns. Arthur was more than happy for that to happen, but Rose kept stepping in and telling him no. Jim was always overhearing the arguments, the insults, between his mother and Arthur, and would sometimes repeat them. He even knew that his baby brother was not from the same dad and not even Arthurs, as the arguments would usually lead back to the origin of the baby. Jim also knew Arthur only married his mum for money but had no idea where the money came from. He would try and protect Roy by comforting him when they were shouting at one another. From an early age, Jim hated both of them.

Wednesday morning, Rose and Arthur were getting ready to head off to the market. Jim was around 10 years old, and Roy was now one. Arthur had asked Jim to stay at the house and look after Roy. He did not understand the commitment and trust that he was being given as he was just a young child himself. He wanted to go and play but was told, as Roy's bigger brother, that he had the duty to look after him when the parents were away. He looked out of the window and watched his parents drive off. He did not know what his brother needed or wanted, so he wrapped him up in a blanket and carried him along the garden path and into the lane where he began walking. He kept lifting Roy up higher to try and stop him from falling from his arms as he was feeling heavy to carry. A horse and cart slowly appeared in the distance coming down the road, Jim stopped it to ask if he and his brother could be taken to the Lawns, as his arms were feeling tired. The driver of the horse and cart was a local man, out of his concern for the children, he lifted Roy and Jim into the cart, and they all headed off in the direction of the Lawns. When they arrived at the Lawns, Jim jumped down and he was passed Roy by the driver. Jim took Roy to the door of the house where James and May greeted them, with a surprised look. The driver began telling them how he was travelling down the road when he saw young Jim struggling to carry what he thought at first to be some groceries. He was telling James how surprised he was seeing the young boy carrying a baby down the road, with no supervision, he was concerned for their safety. James and May could not thank him enough for helping the two of them and bringing them to the Lawns. May took the baby from Jim's arms and gave him a cuddle. She wanted to holler at Jim for his actions but could see he was upset. "What has upset you Jim," May asked, but he did not say anything. She asked again in a gentle voice, so he told her how horrible Arthur was to him, and how he treats his mummy. He knew where Roy was from, who he was, and that they were receiving money to keep him. This was the first time James had heard this story, what Jim was saying, and he believed every word. Although May knew that some of what Jim was saying was not the full truth, she told him to sit by the table and she would cut him some cake.

As the morning passed, Elizabeth came back from the market with a few bags of groceries and was pleasantly surprised to see the two boys at the table drinking milk. She asked Jim, "where is your mum and Arthur?" May jumped in first and told her what had happened. James was angry about what he had heard from Jim, he asked Elizabeth if she knew the full story about how Arthur treats Rose. Elizabeth began acting innocent but knew that her husband was outraged.

May tried to comfort her father and justify why they had not told him. Elizabeth told him how she felt ashamed by what Rose had done in London, sleeping with a Royal Prince for a fur coat. James immediately stopped Elizabeth when she mentioned Rose sleeping with a prince. The stories he had been told by Jim and May minutes before, did not mention anything about Roy not being Arthur's. James demanded that Elizabeth told him the full story from the beginning, she asked May to take the two boys outside so she could explain everything she knew. Jim said he did not need to go outside and began showing off, childishly saying that he knew more than them as he hears everything his mummy and Arthur argue about. "Arthur sleeps downstairs most nights and shouts at mummy and calls her nasty names and she goes to bed crying," Jim shouted. Elizabeth was always protective over Jim and was saddened to hear he had witnessed all of this. She told him that children are to be seen and not heard, to go outside and play and she would be out there soon. May held Jim's hand and picked up Roy, she took them both outside so her mother could tell her father everything she knew. Elizabeth told James how Rose had met the prince when in London, she began sleeping with the prince whilst staying at York House. She explained how Roy was the child of the Prince of Wales, and that Arthur had agreed to marry Rose to save her shame. He agreed to the marriage as he would come into money, which he wanted more than anything else to buy a farm. James felt embarrassed that he did not know what was happening behind his back. Elizabeth could understand how James felt but thought his anger was getting in the way of reasoning. All they could see was that Rose was not being a proper mother to Jim or Roy and she should not be with Arthur from the way he was acting.

# Chapter 35

# THE RAGE WITHIN

That afternoon at the Lawns, Rose rushed through the door, wailing, "Mum, I have lost the kids, they are not at home." James told Rose to calm down, "they are out in the garden with May." His annoyance towards her took over as he explained, "a man heading from Hoarwithy into town found them on the road, and his concern led him to come here, you left that young boy and a baby at home on their own! What possessed you to do that?" Rose wiped the tears from her face and looked at her father, seeing his disappointment. It was something she was not used to seeing in him and could not remember the last time this happened. "Whose idea was this Rose? Yours, or that husband of yours? Where is he?" Rose told him that Arthur was waiting outside with the horse, he wants to go and look for Jim and Roy. "Of course he is. The new caring father does not want to lose his cash cow." Rose's shoulders dropped slightly as she sighed out knowing that the children were safe. She knew that it was not all positive, her father had found out about everything to do with Roy. James told Rose to call Arthur in from the outside, as he wanted to have a word with him, Rose refused as James was still angry. He then asked Elizabeth to call Arthur, who moved to the door, "Arthur you better come here right now, the children are here!" she shouted. Arthur came strutting into the house, "When I get home that boy is going to feel the end of my belt, making us worry like that," he remarked. This angered

James and before Arthur had even stopped, he was pushed so hard that he fell back into the chair and bounced off onto the floor. Shocked and shaken, Arthur did not know what had just happened, James grabbed him by the shirt pulling him up off the ground, ripping off some of the buttons. The two stood there face to face. Elizabeth and Rose stood by and watched with amazement as this unfolded. Arthur didn't struggle, he was afraid and shocked by James's actions. James pulled Arthur closer so they were nose to nose and through gritted teeth, told Arthur that if he ever laid a finger on either of the boys, let alone use a belt on them, he would do the same to him. Arthur could see James was serious and promised not to touch either of them. He was shaken and with Rose they quickly got on to the cart with the boys, leaving in the direction of home. A word was not said on the journey home, Jim sat in the back of the cart, chewing on a piece of straw from the previous day's work. Jim was afraid to say anything as he knew he was to blame for granddad's brawl with Arthur.

They arrived back at Middle Mill, it was dusk, the fires needed lighting inside to warm the house. Arthur set about lighting the fire, Rose lit the oil lamp that was sat on the table and gave Jim bread and cheese for supper. She acted gentle in her manner towards Jim, the already nervous child, and told him to go straight to his room once he had finished. Jim did not argue as he knew he would be in trouble with Arthur if he answered back. Rose gave Roy a change of clothes, a bottle of milk, and put him to bed. She sat with him, smoothing his head until he was fast asleep, she told Jim not to get out of bed and to let his brother sleep. Jim promised to stay in bed as he pulled the cover over his head. Rose gently closed the door and went downstairs to Arthur; he was sitting in his chair glaring at the fire. She could feel the tension and before Arthur could say anything, Rose spoke. "Well, father knows everything now, so if you don't change your ways, I will leave you and go back home." Arthur was not impressed with Rose's threat. "Do you really think he would have you back knowing what you are?" Arthur moaned. Rose said she believed her family would have her back home, now they all knew the truth about her baby. She mentioned how the money that came in for Roy belonged to her, and if she went back to the Lawns, the payments would go too. Arthur slumped down in his chair knowing he would have to change his attitude towards Rose and the children, or lose his farm, as the next payment would be due very soon.

The next morning, Jim was up early and went downstairs to find Arthur asleep in the chair. He crept around the room not to wake him, afraid that if he did, he would get a clip around the ear. He heard his mother go into his bedroom to attend to Roy who was crying and screaming for attention. This woke up Arthur, who gave a stern look towards Jim, he wanted to give him a leathering for walking to the Lawns, but then remembered what James had said. "About yesterday boy! I don't want you ever to do that again." Jim answered that he would not do it again, he just did not like being left on his own, he wanted to visit granny and auntie May. Rose was coming down the stairs with Roy in her arms, she said to Arthur and Jim she would get breakfast ready. She put Roy into his highchair and then drew a pan of water to boil some eggs. Jim and Roy both loved to have egg's and soldiers for breakfast. "Arthur, would you fetch some wood and light the fire?" she asked him. Arthur did as he was told, he knew things had to change as he did not want to lose out on the money they were receiving. He did not want to lose the farm so offered to help in the house, Rose told him she had it all under control. "Very well, after breakfast, I will walk around the fields to make sure the fences and gates are good, if that's alright with you." I was wondering if, perhaps, Jim would like to help?" Rose told him that was a great idea, Jim was still feeling nervous about being alone with Arthur in case he hit him. "How long will you be gone for?" Rose asked. "Why?" Arthur questioned. "Would you like me to pack a sandwich for you?" Rose replied. Arthur gave a slight smile and told Rose that it would not take too long, and they would be back before lunch. Jim nervously put on his coat, Rose looked at him and gave him a smile and told him to be a good boy, then looked at Arthur and said, "fresh start." Arthur didn't reply as he closed the door behind them.

Rose carried on doing the housework throughout the morning and playing with Roy until he fell asleep. She carried him upstairs and put him down for his nap. He was no longer sleeping in the drawer of the dresser, Rose enjoyed how the room appeared now that all the drawers were closed. She still wanted to buy a rug for the floor and fabric to make curtains for the small sitting room, this would make the room look cosy. She was hoping that when the money came, Arthur would have enough to buy his cow, and that there would be some money left to buy some things that were needed for the house. Rose went downstairs and put a large saucepan of stew on the fire to cook. She sat there enjoying the silence as Roy slept, with Arthur and Jim out on the farm. Rose's mind started to wonder; she began thinking about London, wondering about how Jean and Lewis were, or if they were even still there at the palace. Since she left London, Rose tried not to think about the Prince of Wales and the way he treated her, but every time she thought of her London adventure, this would lead her back to him. She thought of the ring and the fur coat all the time, dreaming about wearing it out in public, to big high-profile events but with each tick of the clock, it would bring her imagination back to reality. Rose looked at the time and decided to go upstairs to Jim's room to look at her coat. She pulled out the once white box from under the bed, as it was now coated in dust. Rose blew the dust off gently, watching as the whiteness of the box return, and opened it to reveal the pristine fur coat. She lifted it out of the box and slid her arms inside, wrapping it around herself as she waltzed around the room in a trance. As she began humming to herself, dreaming about being at a gala ball, she heard the voices of Jim and Arthur come into the house; quickly Rose whipped off the coat and threw it into the box, and slid it under the bed with her foot. The footsteps of Jim came rushing upstairs and into the room, "What are you doing in here mum?" Rose brushed her hands across Jim's bedding and replied, "I'm making your bed," as she ushered him back downstairs, Rose followed him down the stairs with Roy in her arms. Arthur said to Rose, "the fences are in good order, ready for purpose, we just need some livestock to put in them now." Rose replied, "we will see what price the cows are making at the cattle market on Wednesday." Arthur was beaming with joy as all he wanted was to have his own heard of cows on the biggest farm. He had the idea that eventually he could have the best milking herd in the whole country. Rose reminded him that we will start small and then make the farm grow, as an acorn into an oak tree. Rose asked Arthur "what breed of cow are you looking for." He replied, "I would like a Hereford cow to start with, a pure bred one, as this would be most appropriate for beef and milk." Arthur then said, "I am going to the Maypole to see Frank to speak to him about getting a cow." He asked Rose if she would like to go with him, but she declined stating that she was going to do the washing, and could he get the bath out of the shed before he left. Arthur was happy that the two of them were talking, not arguing, life felt good for once. He brought the bath into the house so Rose could do the washing and left to go and see Frank. Rose on the other hand, was just wanting to get back upstairs to put the fur coat away properly so it would not crease in the box.

Rose told Jim to stay downstairs, he could have one of the rock cakes she made earlier that morning. She rushed upstairs and got the box out from underneath the bed, folding the fur coat neatly and placing it back in the box. She then slid the box under the bed until she felt it touch the wall. Pulling the cover over the bed, she left the room and went downstairs, Jim was sat at the table eating the rock cake silently. "Well, that's taken you long enough to eat, do you not like it?" She got closer and saw that most of the rock cakes had gone. Jim had eaten nearly all of them. "Where the hell have the cakes gone?" She roared. Jim pointed at Roy and said he ate them all. Rose walked around the table to Jim and gave him a slap around the ear. Jim tried to duck, stepping back, and standing on Roy who was on the floor. Roy screamed in pain and Rose rushed to pick him up. Jim must have broken the silver rattle when he stood on Roy, as it lay there in two pieces. Rose was not happy seeing this, she lashed out at Jim catching him on his cheek, then she screamed for him to, "get out now!" Jim ran out of the backdoor and hid in the shed until Arthur returned that afternoon.

Rose was indoors holding Roy and crying over the broken rattle. She seemed more distraught about the rattle, rather than Jim standing on Roy. She wrapped Roy in the blanket that she had had from the palace, then nursed him until he settled. She sat there holding the rattle looking at the broken state it was in, not knowing if it could be repaired. Remembering the day, she had received it, and the lifestyle she had left in London. How she was still wanted the London life of glamour, but realised she was now just a farmer's wife.

Arthur returned home from the Maypole still beaming with excitement at the fact that he was getting a cow. He asked Rose how the day had gone, she put on a smile and said, "the same as usual, housework and childminding." He asked where Jim was, and Rose told him that Jim was in the shed waiting for him to return. She explained that he ate most of the cakes and lied to her face, trying to blame Roy so she gave him a smack across the head. "He's such a bloody liar," Arthur grumbled. Arthur expressed that he was going to cause a lot of trouble, asking Rose if they could send him over to live at the Lawns with his granny. Rose did consider it but was worried about what her parents and May would think about them abandoning Jim. Rose went to the backdoor and shouted for Jim to come in. He was hungry, all he had eaten that day were the rock cakes, he thought he was being called in for his supper and rushed in. Rose told him he was to go to bed with no supper and ordered him to his room. Jim said he was hungry and put his hand out, asking for some bread, but Rose pushed his hand away and growled at him to go to his room. Rose continued making Arthur his dinner and feeding Roy. Arthur knew that Jim must have really upset his mother, and cautiously asked, "Are you not going to give the boy anything to eat then?" Rose snapped at Arthur, telling him that Jim could go hungry as he was a thief, as he had eaten most of the cakes. As Rose sat in the chair with Roy on her lap, trying to rock him to sleep. Arthur said, "it's a bit early for the boys to be going to bed." Rose defended her decision, "I have had enough of these bloody kids all day. They get on my nerves all the time." Roy held out his arms to go to Arthur. "Do you want to hold him," Arthur hesitatingly held out his arms and replied, "I'm not sure I know how." Rose placed Roy on Arthur's lap and gave him a bottle of milk, showing him how to hold and feed Roy with the bottle. Roy slowly fell asleep on Arthur with the bottle slipping out of his mouth. Rose told him to take him up to his bedroom and put him into his cot. He gently lifted Roy, not to wake him, and picked up a chunk of bread from the kitchen for Jim. On entering the bedroom Arthur silently nudged Jim and handed him the piece of bread, telling him not to tell his mother. Jim snatched it from Arthur's hands with a smile and slid under his covers to eat it. As Arthur put Roy into his cot, he noticed how high the sides were, thinking to himself that they needed to be lowered, and that he would fix them tomorrow. He left the room as he said goodnight to the boys.

# Chapter 36

# KEEP THE MONEY COMING

The next day a man from the Palace was due to bring the payment for Edward (Roy). No one from London knew he was registered as Roy, although Mr Wigram had specified this in the arrangement, as he had to become Arthur's son officially, Rose had not informed him. Rose cleaned the house ready for the palace representative to arrive with the payment. It was just before lunch that they heard a car pull up and a short thick set man, wearing a bowler hat, came towards the house, leaving his driver waiting in the car. Rose went to the door and opened it for this pompous man who did not introduce himself other than announcing he was from the Palace. Rose said her good mornings and offered him a cup of tea as he entered. He looked around the room observing everything in sight. Although the house was clean most of the furniture looked pretty worn. "No thank you," he said for the tea, he then said, "I have been asked to see how Edward is." Rose picked him up off the floor, he was laying on a few cushions playing with a rattle. The man from London looked at him. "The boy looks well, is everything alright with him?" Rose was surprised by the question, "Whatever do you mean?" She asked. "His health, is he well? Does he need anything?" Arthur was stood by the backdoor listening and rushed to Rose's side at that question, interrupting their discussion. "Yes. We could do with a new cot for him. The one I made is too high and it's difficult to get him in and out. Here, follow me, I'll show you." The man followed Arthur upstairs to see the cot for himself. Arthur explained the way it worked, the man nodded, "I see," he said, as he looked around the rest of the room. He then made his way downstairs and took another look at Roy as he handed an envelope to Rose. The man made his excuses to leave and walked out of the door, towards the car. He was here no more than fifteen minutes, and after he left, they began counting the money in the envelope. Arthur continuously asking Rose if it was all there and for her to count it again. Rose was annoyed at Arthur coming into the room when the man was there. "I told you and Jim to stay outside when these people come." Arthur apologised to Rose but said that when he heard him ask if there was anything they needed, that he needed to ask for the cot for Roy. Rose could not be cross with Arthur, he had asked for something for Roy and not for himself which made a change. Rose said, "On Wednesday, we will go and buy that cow you want." She handed Arthur enough money to buy his cow. "The rest must do us until the next quarter," Rose said, as Arthur went to put his money away.

Three days after the Palace representative visited, a delivery van turned up with a brand-new cot for Roy, with blankets for the cot, and a set of sheets for a single bed and also a pillowcase. Although these other items were not asked for, the visitor had taken it upon himself to send a pillowcase and sheets for Jim's bed. Rose and Arthur were happy with the man's kindness. "I should have said the kids needed a sofa to sit on. They would have bought us one of those," Arthur joked. Rose laughed at Arthur's statement and was pleased with the gifts and thought that he may be on to something.

Wednesday morning, Arthur was up at the crack of dawn, and ready to head to the market to buy his cow. At the market, he looked at the cattle, thinking he was now as wise as any farmer to know a good cow from a bad cow. He had the money in his pocket and tried to make several deals to buy a cow. He wanted a pure Hereford Heifer if he could get one, but they were too expensive. He ended up buying a Hereford cross cow who had a calf at foot, he was pleased with his first purchase. Arthur found Rose and rushed with excitement to tell her what he had just bought. She was as pleased as he was, she was thinking of all the fresh milk they would now have for the house. On the way home, they stopped by the second-hand store. It had a few bits of furniture but nothing Rose wanted. There were some pictures and a couple of old rugs, one rug had seen better days, but Rose wanted both of them. As they were about to leave, she noticed in the corner of the store, a roll of fabric. She could not see the pattern as it was rolled inside out. She asked the storekeeper how much it was, he replied, you could have it at a reasonable price, make me an offer. It had slight water damage and could not be sold as new. Rose was happy to make an offer and to finally have some fabric. The journey home was completely different to what they normally had, the atmosphere was positive, and they all felt happy. Rose was holding Roy and Jim on the back of the cart, dreaming of what she could make with the fabric and Arthur was excited for the cow and calf he had purchased.

Friday morning arrived and so did Arthur's cow and calf. He put them in the paddock and stood admiring them for a long time, watching the calf leap and play around the cow. Rose was outside unrolling her fabric on the lawn, not knowing when it was going to reach the end as she kept unrolling it. She could see the water damage on the floral design. It had a cream-coloured background, but the water had made rusty lines all over the fabric. Rose measured different lengths and cut it whilst it was flat on the grass. Jim wandered over, curious about the fabric, "What is that for mum?" He asked. "This is for curtains in the sitting room, that over there is for the kitchen and the rest is going to be bed covers. If there is any left, I will make you a shirt and Roy a dress." Jim looked at it poking out his tongue in disgust, "I'm not wearing that. It's yucky." Rose told him to wait and see, "when it's made you may like it then." Rose picked up all the fabric, folding each set of cut curtains into different piles as not to mix them up. She could not wait to get started on the sewing. Later that evening when the children were in bed, Rose and Arthur were sat chatting downstairs. Rose was sewing the first pair of curtains next to the glowing, roaring fire, which was lighting the whole room, and all seemed right with the world for the first time. "If I had a treadle sewing machine like the one in the Palace, I could have run up these curtains in half the time." Arthur looked to Rose annoyed, "Why did you have to spoil the evening?" She was caught by surprise by his questioning, "What do you mean?" Rose asked. "Well, we have had a good evening and then you have to go and mention them at the bloody Palace." Rose defended her initial comment by reminding Arthur that she did not mention anyone from the Palace, and how he was able to have the money to buy his cow. "Do you think we should ask Mr Wigram for some more things?" Rose suggested. "You know, like what we need? If you ask him nicely, do you think he would supply them? When you think about it, we could do with a lot of stuff for Roy." Rose left the room with the kettle to make Arthur a cup of tea, leaving him to think over her suggestion.

A week passed and Arthur was now thinking he was a man of means, a down payment on a farm, buying a cow and looking after the son of a prince. He thought he had the right to ask for more money and things from the palace. He sent a telegram to Mr Wigram at the Palace asking for a meeting for himself and Rose. He wrote offering to travel to the Palace at any time that was convenient to him so they could discuss the child. Mr Wigram replied immediately as the child's welfare was utmost, although Arthur had given no details of why they should meet. Rose and Arthur had arranged for the children to stay at the neighbouring farm with Mrs Brooks, whilst they were away in London.

Travelling to London was not as exciting for Rose as it once was. When they arrived in London, they decided to walk some of the way from Paddington train station to the Palace, to enjoy the sights and sounds weaving between people and zigzagging down different streets. They arrived at the Palace on-time for their appointment. They were taken to the office of Mr Wigram and told to wait, as he was not currently available. They sat there patiently waiting, when the door finally opened, they were surprised to find they were sat in front of King George. Rose and Arthur jumped straight to their feet like a spring had ejected them from their seat. Rose curtsied low down to the floor as Arthur bowed his head. His Majesty looked as surprised to find them there as they were to see his Majesty. Arthur began speaking, "Good morning, sir, I am Arthur. I collected birds for you at the shoots." The King clearly did not recognise Arthur or remember who he was at the shoots, but he smiled politely. Rose introduced herself and curtsied again. King George asked the two of them if they had seen Mr Wigram and, both coordinated there answer "no sir." Rose introduced herself again, "I'm Rose sir. Rose Davies as was, now Powell. His Majesty's eyes lifted as he recognised that name. "I thought everything was sorted with that issue," He confessed. Arthur joined the conversation, "Sir, I am now a man of means and looking after your grandson as my own child." King George's face turned into a deep frown, and he turned towards the door as if he was about to leave, when Mr Wigram entered.

He looked embarrassed at the sight of seeing Arthur and Rose in the presence of King George. He turned to the King and bowed his head, "Your Majesty. I am so sorry for my absence; how may I help you?" He could see him looking at Rose and Arthur. "This is the Powell's, your Majesty." As he was introducing them, Arthur held out his hand to shake the hand of King George. "Yes" Said His Majesty. Arthur interrupted again, "I was just telling the King, as I am now a man of means and looking after his grandson, Edward, as my own son, I think it's only fair he be brought up in a family with a title." At that point, you could have knocked Mr Wigram down with a feather, he looked like he was going to faint. "A title?" he gasped. At that point, King George left the room without saying another word. For some reason, Arthur then bowed to Mr Wigram, thanking him for all his kindness and how he and Rose appreciated everything he had done for them so far. Mr Wigram could see Arthur was trying to be respectable and he appreciated that. The meeting continued for over an hour, and they discussed most things concerning Edward. "I will do my best to raise the boy right sir," Arthur stated. As they stood up to leave, Mr Wigram shook Arthur's hand, and this brought a smile to Arthur's face. Mr Wigram handed Rose and Arthur a five-pound note for the train fare home. He could see the excitement on Arthur's face, as he was thanking Mr Wigram repeatedly.

As they left the Palace and began walking back to the train station, Arthur asked Rose if she would like to have tea at a café, something they had never done before. Rose was more than happy to accept Arthur's invitation. As they entered the café, a waitress greeted them and asked if they would like a table, she showed them to a small table for two near the window. Rose and Arthur began to take in the ambiance around the café, admiring the pictures on the walls, creating a cosy atmosphere. The tables around the café were placed in such a way that some seated four people and others seated two. They all had matching tablecloths and had posies of flowers in vases, at the centre of each table. Rose was excited that every table had matching crockery, plus a matching teapot. This is something she had never seen before and knew it would be something she would want at home. The waitress, in a black dress, a white pinny with matching band on her head, came to the table. "Good afternoon Sir, Madam, are you ready for me to take your order?" Arthur looked at Rose's beaming smile and looked back at the waitress, "We would like tea for two, please, and a slice of cake each." The waitress took their order before replying, "sir, which cake would you like?" Arthur and Rose looked at the cakes on the serving trolley, taking their time to look at so many cakes presented before them. They both asked for slices of the Victoria sandwich. As they waited, they were gazing out of the window and quietly commenting on the people passing by. The waitress placed the teapot and cups on the table and went to get the cake slices. They both turned to the table, Rose began pouring the tea before the waitress arrived with their cakes. They looked at one another after seeing the huge slices of cake that had been put in front of them. Rose told Arthur that she thought it would be better to share a slice and take one home and began wrapping it in her handkerchief she pulled from her handbag. Rose then cut the remaining slice of cake in two and put one half on Arthur's plate and continued pouring the tea into the cups. She was fascinated by the whole experience of pouring the tea into the Fine Bone China cup. Arthur waited for Rose to finish pouring the tea, he leaned forward holding out his hand, Rose placed her hand in his, and Arthur gently squeezed as they smiled to one another. When they finished the cake and drank every drop of tea from the teapot, Arthur pulled out the five-pound note and held it for everyone to see. The waitress took the money and gave him the change, "Thank you for visiting sir, we hope to see you again soon." Arthur stood and bent his arm for Rose to hold as they left the café. Arthur was buzzing, "did you hear that? She called me sir and hopes to see us again, she can see we are class." Rose was telling Arthur about the teapot and cups and how she wishes she could have a set of her own. Arthur was still in a world of his own and said "I think that's the kind of place where all the toffs go. We will have to definitely come here again."

# Chapter 37

# A CHANGE OF TONE

On the journey home from London, Arthur continued talking about being called sir, and how it now made him feel. "I am going to be a gentleman and you a lady," he told Rose. "We can work at this; we have everything to gain." She was pleased to hear he was at last interested in doing something for the both of them. Rose took the opportunity to express her interest as Arthur was in a good mood, "I think we will call Roy buy his full name, as in Roy Albert and not just his first name. I think it will distinguish him from others. What do you think?" Arthur agreed "It does have a better ring to it than Roy. It sounds as if he comes from a better class."

When they got back to Hereford, they picked up Jim and Roy from Brooks Farm. Rose thanked Mrs Brooks for looking after the children and offered to make repairs or alterations on Mrs Brooks' daughters' dresses. Mrs Brooks thanked Rose for the kind offering, she said that it was nice having the boys, and the girls have enjoyed playing with them. As soon as they got back to Middle Mill, Arthur and Jim went across the field to check on the cow and calf. Arthur told Jim that the calf was coming along well, "Well boy, we will have to buy more of these if we are going to be proper farmers, Jim nodded in agreement. As they walked back to the house, Rose had lit the fire to heat the water. Rose had the water boiling, she looked out the window and saw Arthur and Jim walking towards the house. Rose shouted out to Arthur to get the tin bath off the wall, as she was going to give the boys a bath before they went to bed.

Rose placed the tin bath in front of the fire and poured the hot water in, she added cold water before Jim stepped in. Rose said to Jim, "Once you have had a bath, I will bath Roy Albert, so don't be long." Jim looked at his mum, "Why Roy Albert? You are not going to call me by my full name, are you?" Rose flicked some water at Jim, "No. I just thought it sounded a bit nicer than Roy, what do you think?" Jim stood still in the tin bath, thinking. "No, I think I will call him Roy," he told his mum, this made Rose chuckle. Jim put out his arms for help to get out of the bath, he then dried himself with the towel. "Are you dry all over?" She asked, as she was rubbing her hand down the middle of his back. He shrugged it off. "Of course, I am dry, I am a big boy now." Jim continued rubbing himself with the towel, she said to him, she did not want him to catch a chill if he had not dried himself properly. Rose lifted Roy Albert and put him into the bath water. He began splashing his chubby hands and kicking his legs in the water, as Rose was holding him, he was wriggling, giggling and chuckled. Roy Albert was enjoying himself in the warm water, when Rose started to lift him from the water he began yelling, so she put him back in for a few more minutes. Rose washed him and then picked him up and shook off the excess water, and he began giggling loud again. She wrapped him in a towel and placed him on her lap. When he was dry and dressed, she asked Arthur if he would like a bath. "Not now," he responded, "I would have had one before you washed the boys in the bath, but not now." Rose got the boys ready for bed and took them upstairs.

When Rose came back down, she began undressing in front of the fire and stood in the bath. She sat down but her knees were close to her chest, there was no room to move. She asked Arthur to add more hot water in to warm it up a little. As he poured in the boiling water from the kettle, it became too hot, and Rose squealed. "Get some cold water!" Arthur ran into the kitchen and picked up the pale of cold water from the sink. As he poured it in, it became too cold, and Rose began complaining. "Right!" Arthur said, "Stand up and we will get this water hot enough for you to have a proper wash. Rose stepped out as Arthur began mixing the hot and cold water into the bath to make it bearable for her to wash. Rose stepped back into the bath and let out a sigh of relief. It was comfortably warming. She sat back down into the bath, wanting to stretch out, but it was not possible. She remembered about the long bath she stretched out in when she was working in London. This bath had two taps on it, one for the hot water and one for the cold water. If you sat in the bath at the Palace, the water would not flow over the sides of the bath. When Rose sat down in her tin bath, the water came right up towards the top. When she stood up, the water would sink back down to half of the size of the tub. She climbed out and dried herself in front of the warm fire, then sitting down on the chair she sat staring into the flames; Watching them beat against the back of the fireplace, punching high, as if they are trying to reach the top of the chimney. Rose then remembered she had to empty the bath. There was no plug with this one. The water had nowhere to go so she called Arthur to help her carry it to the back door so they could pour it outside. They began lifting it with a handle each, but the water swished side to side, almost spilling over the top. Rose told Arthur that she would have to empty it using a bucket instead. Rose took the cold-water bucket back to the kitchen and emptied it down the sink. Making multiple trips back to the front room to collect the water from the bath until the bath was completely empty. Arthur then took the bath outside to the shed. Rose collapsed into her seat by the fire, looking at Arthur, she said to him, "The bathroom at the Palace, oh Arthur, it had a proper bath with taps and a toilet that flushed. You pulled the long chain, and the water came rushing in. Not like the shed we have outside." Arthur told Rose that he knows it is not what she wants in life, but they have more at that point than he ever thought they would. "When is the next payment for Roy Albert?" he asked. Rose lifted her head in curiosity, "Not for a few months, it is every quarter, why? What do you want to buy now, another cow and calf?" Arthur told her he wanted to buy a car to make things easier to take them around in. Rose liked the idea and told him to start looking for one in the next few months. "I wonder if we will hear about the title," Arthur expressed to Rose, but she told him that it could take time as they took their time with everything else.

A tin bath of that period

# Chapter 38

# LORD GLASBURY

The following morning the Postman arrived with a letter for Rose. Rose knew as soon as she saw the front of the envelope that it was Jean Hughes by the handwriting. She waited for the boys to settle down, Jim was playing with his wooden toy car, running it up and down Roy's legs, making him laugh. Rose asked Jim if he was ready to set off for school, as time was getting on. She then sat in the chair and opened it, to read what Jean had written. The letter was to tell Rose what she had overheard at the Palace in London.

The letter read,

---

*My dear Rose,*

*Today I overheard Mr Hardinge speaking to Mr Wigram who said that the King had decided to grant Arthur a title. Mr Hardinge was shocked and openly disagreed with the idea, but Mr Wigram said it was for the best and things should be left as they now stand, his Majesty had his own reasons for doing so. He could see Mr Hardinge was in shock and patted him on the shoulder, "Ours is not to reason why he said." Mr Hardinge mumbled he could not understand what things were coming to, if all unsundry was to get a title. Then Mr Wigram said, "I wouldn't have done what he did for anything, would you?" Mr Hardinge shook his head. I quickly moved on down the corridor, but I do believe he will get the title he so wanted. I hope I have not spoiled the surprise, My Lady.*

*Yours as always.*

*Jean*

*P.S. I will keep my ears open and will let you know if I hear anything else.*

---

Rose went to find Arthur, shouting at the back of the house, but there was no sign of him. She shouted, calling out his name, over and over. In the distance, she could see him working in the field, so waved the letter above her head. Arthur waved and headed home, he began picking up his pace getting faster as he got closer to the house. He asked, "what is it," as he was catching his breath. She told him that Jean had written, explaining that Mr Wigram and Hardinge were talking about a title given to you by the King. Rose went on to say, from what Jean has written, they were not very happy about it, Hardinge does not think we are the right sort to have a title. After Arthur had caught his breath, he stood tall and proud with his head held high, "Well, this is it Rose, what do you think of marrying me now? A man of means and a bloody title. That will be a shock to everyone around here. Don't you think?" Rose looked at Arthur and told him not to say a word to anyone until they have it in writing from the Palace. Arthur smiled and walked into the house.

Arthur and Rose were unsettled for days after receiving the letter from Jean. They were waiting to get that all important letter from the Palace, several weeks passed and then a letter turned up, an official letter asking Rose and Arthur to attend the Palace. Arthur had a new suit for the occasion and a pair of leather shoes. He was pleased as he did not often have the opportunity to wear shoes, he had mainly worn boots in the past. Rose made a new two piece and she looked beautiful with her matching hat and gloves. The boys went to stay with Mrs Brooks while they took the trains to London. They were surprised to see so many people all dressed up in their smartest clothes. Arthur and Rose were ushered off to a small side room, when they entered, there stood the King, who looked at both Arthur and Rose. In the room there were a few people standing around, focusing on the King, this included Mr Hardinge and Mr Wigram. Arthur looking all the gentleman in his smart suit, knelt before the King, and was made a Baronet. He was granted the title of Glasbury (pronounced Glazebury). This itself meant so much to Arthur. He was bestowed with a large medallion on a ribbon, which was placed around his neck, a few words were spoken, and then the King left the room. There were other men asking Arthur all sorts of questions, Rose excused herself from the room, as she needed the bathroom. She could hear Arthur describing many things, to a man from the Heraldry, and then he said, "I would like an acorn, as out of small acorns, large trees grow." She did not have a clue what Arthur was talking about. As she left the room, she caught Mr Wigram's eye. "Are you alright, Rose?" Rose nodded, "Yes sir, I'm just needing to use the lavatory and I cannot think how to get to the servant's quarters from here." Mr Wigram smiled, "You must use the guest restroom. I will show you where to find them." Mr Wigram opened the door and pointed down the corridor, giving Rose the full directions of where to find the restroom.

Rose walked along the corridor, slowly looking at everything and everyone, giving a smile to the ladies who looked at her. She was so happy, being there as an invited guest rather than working as a seamstress. As a group of people walked towards her, she recognised a voice within the group. She stopped to let them pass only to catch the eye of the Prince of Wales. He looked at her and with a smile, and commented, "Well, hello wosey posey, what are you doing here?" She bowed her head slightly, almost cowering away, but she could see his group looking her up and down. She felt intimidated and did not know what to say. The prince continued talking, "I heard you married a farmer, and why are you in this part of the house? The servant's quarters are elsewhere, and he sniggered with his friends. She tensed her jaw and looked at him, straight in the eye. "You are right David; I did marry a farmer and he is the one who has taken on your son as his own. The baby you put in my belly when I worked here at York House. I am not a servant; my husband has been granted a title so your son will have something to grow up with." The Prince of Wales could not find the words to say at her announcement, and told his group of friends, who were already shocked by Rose's outburst, to continue walking. Rose began to walk towards the bathroom as the prince grabbed her arm, "how dare you make a fool of me," I will make sure you, your husband, and that bastard child, will never have existed." He let go of Rose with a force that made her fall to the floor. Gasps echoed through the corridor and some people could not believe what they witnessed. Mr Wigram heard the commotion and rushed towards Rose. The Prince of Wales walked past him but did not say a word, he continued through the corridors with a stern look, heading towards his friends. Mr Wigram helped Rose to her feet. With tears running down her face, she thanked him and rushed off towards the restroom. Arthur was still chatting as fast as he could to several different people in the side room. Rose on returning to the side room, told Mr Wigram what the prince had said to her. He did not have an answer, he knew how childish the prince could be, and sometimes he would say things, but never followed through with his threats; Rose was not so sure about this. Once Rose and Arthur had finished talking to other guests in the room, Mr Wigram took them to a car that was waiting at the front of the Palace. He told the driver to take them to the train station. As they began getting into the car, Mr Wigram advised Rose and Arthur to not have any contact with the prince. Arthur was bubbling with joy from their day at the Palace and told Rose everything she had missed in the room. "So, what happened to you?" He asked, "you missed a lot." Rose did not want to explain in front of the driver, "we will talk about it later on the train."

When they arrived at Paddington station they had to wait for their train, Rose was feeling agitated and wanted to get home. Arthur told her he had met a Herald and that he was going to draw up a family Crest and a Coat of Arms. He went on to mention about the acorn and the farm and how he had been asked so many questions, at one point he thought his head would spin. He mentioned to Rose how Mr Hardinge tutted and whinged if Arthur said the wrong thing, which was every sentence. He knew Mr Hardinge disliked him because he had been granted a title by the King. Rose was edgy and anxious as she spoke to Arthur about the coming together, she had in the corridor. "I saw David, he threatened us. Me, you, and the baby." Rose could see the concern in Arthur's face. "What did he mean by this?" Arthur replied. Rose told him she had no idea what it meant, Mr Wigram had told her not to have any further contact with the prince, he would forget, as he said it in anger. Arthur was concerned about their safety but could not understand what the cause was to make a threat. "What caused him to be like that?" he asked. Rose told Arthur about her encounter with the prince in the corridor on the way to the bathroom, and how he was with a group of friends belittling her. She told him they were getting a title for looking after his son and that is when he became angry. Rose showed Arthur her arm where the prince had grabbed her with such force. It had several small bruises on it. Arthur became angry, pacing around the platform. "Well, that's the end of that then. I liked the idea of being someone." Rose could see Arthur was getting upset and tried reassuring him, "Well, we haven't lost anything yet. The title was off King George, not him. Mr Wigram said he was just ranting, and he is known for doing that. Listen to what Mr Wigram says and see how it goes from there." The first part of their train journey they both had little to talk about, Arthur was thinking things over in his mind, what would happen if they lost everything. From Newport to Hereford, they both dozed off, exhausted from their exhilarating day.

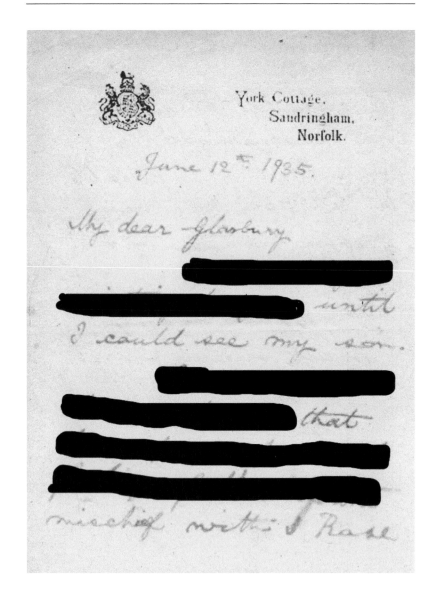

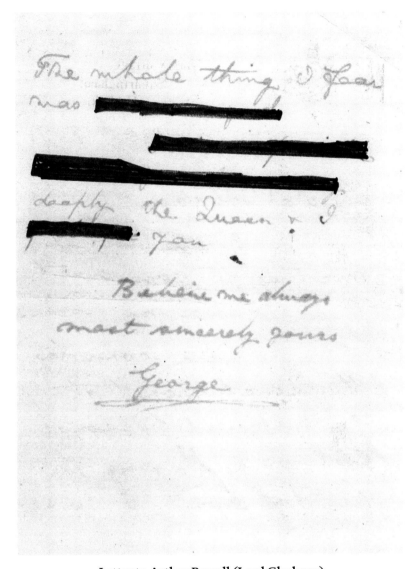

**Letter to Arthur Powell (Lord Glasbury)**

# Chapter 39

# A FARMER WITH A TITLE

Arthur had arranged for Frank to pick them up from Hereford station. Rose was worried Arthur was going to tell Frank what had happened with the prince, but he kept silent about these events. Frank drove them to Brooks Farm to pick up the boys, along the way they chatted with him, about the things they had seen in London. Mr and Mrs Brooks greeted them at the door and were impressed by how well Rose and Arthur were dressed. Arthur could not wait to tell them where they had been and for what reason. He showed them his Baronetcy medallion that was granted by King George V. It was something that few people would ever get to see. "And what did you have to do for one of those then?" Mr Brooks asked. Rose and Arthur did not have a planned answer to explain how they got it, Arthur looked puzzled about what to answer, Rose quickly changed the subject, asking if the children had behaved themselves, and if the family were well. After a short conversation, Rose told them how it had been such a busy day and was feeling tired, so she ushered Arthur and Jim to the door and picked up Roy Albert who was falling asleep. Rose thanked the family for being there to look after the children and they left the house. Frank was waiting outside for them with the car and drove them all back to the Mill. Rose invited Frank in for a cup of tea, as a thank you for picking them up and driving them home. They began chatting for a while and he also asked why Arthur was granted such an honour as they were a farming family who had no status in society. "Well, remember we do have two farms, Frank. That's a lot more than most." Frank still did not believe that having two farms would be a reason for someone to have a title of that calibre but did not bother asking again.

The next thing for Rose and Arthur to do was to tell Rose's parents. Rose wondered how they were going to react. Arthur was preening around like a peacock in his new suit and leather shoes. "Let's go and tell your parents now," he begged Rose. Rose told him to get changed first as she did not want him to mark his clothes. He kept hurrying Rose as he wanted to tell as many people as possible before they heard it from someone else. Rose asked Jim to go to the car while she put Roy Albert's coat on and wrapped him in a blanket. "I don't think the King looked very well." Rose remarked. Arthur thought the King looked all right, although he did not make conversation with him. Arthur placed his Baronetcy around his neck, lifted his chin and put on a posh voice, "Well, my girl, one has never seen one of these before." Rose burst out laughing and put on an exaggerated voice, "you don't talk like that, me lord." Arthur and Rose erupted with laughter. As Arthur brushed himself down, he looked at Roy Albert, patted his head, and whispered, "You, my boy, are going to get me everything." He kissed him gently on the top of his head. Rose picked up Roy Albert and carried him to the door following Arthur and Jim to the car.

In the car, Rose found herself staring at Roy. Arthur noticed this and asked if everything was all right with him? Gazing at her baby boy she replied, "He's fine. He reminds me so much of his father." She then realised what she had said, as Jim was in the back of the car, she looked at Arthur who did not respond to her statement. When they pulled into the Lawns, Jim got out and ran in to see his grandmother and aunty May. Rose and Arthur walked through the door and her mother asked if they wanted a cup of tea. May greeted them both with affection, "Where have you been all dressed up?" Rose waited for Arthur to tell them about the day. "I've been to the Palace," Rose lowered her eyebrows, "No, we have been to the Palace, and we have something to tell you. Arthur has been granted a title of Baronetcy by King George himself. He is now Lord Glasbury." They all looked at each other, "Well I never Rose. Where have you really been?" May asked. Rose took a breath and sighed, "We really went to the Palace to see King George, and yes, Arthur is really a Lord. He is now Lord Glasbury. Elizabeth and May knew then that Rose was telling the truth. Arthur proudly showed them his Baronetcy. With a shocked look on her face, May asked, "Is that real gold?" Arthur nodded, "I think so, it's probably worth a bit." Rose interrupted, "I don't care how much it is worth, you are not selling it, Where's dad?" Rose asked. James was outside working.

They waited for James to return home. Eventually he returned, tired and dirty, he did not look pleased to see they were there. He noticed Arthur in his suit and said, "where have you been, to see the King?" He burst out laughing, before continuing, "A bit dressed up to visit us, aren't you?" Arthur told him they had been to London to see the King, and how he had been given a title. He then introduced himself to James as Lord Glasbury. James could not believe what Arthur was saying, Rose took hold of her father's arm, "dad, we really have been to the Palace and King George made him a baronet. He knelt before the King, and he touched him with his sword and that was that. We have a crest and a family coat of arms." James put his hand on his head as if to doff his cap, "Do we have to bow to you now then? Did you get any money with it?" Arthur could tell that James was not taking it seriously so responded, "No, I did get this." As he held out his medallion. Before James could say anything, Arthur continued,

"And yes, it is real gold and Rose has said we are not selling it." Elizabeth asked what happened and what it was like, so Rose began telling her of the journey to London before Elizabeth butted in saying to Rose, she did not want to hear about the journey, she wanted to hear about the Palace and the title. Rose explained that they were taken to a private room and not in public with all the other guests. She could not explain why they had a private meeting with the King but that is how it went. She described the room in great detail, how the curtains went from the ceiling to the floor, the large gold framed paintings of landscapes and horses. They could see Rose and Arthur had a wonderful time. Elizabeth could tell something was distracting Rose, as she skipped between the happenings of the day. Rose was careful not to mention the part where she bumped into the Prince of Wales. Jim was playing with May, when he stopped, and as he looked at his mum, he whispered something into May's ear. Rose was wondering what was so secret, Jim had to tell May, was it what he had overheard in the car, about Roy Albert looking like his father. Rose continued explaining about the Palace and everything she had seen, but the story started to repeat itself. James started to focus on the fire in the room, and Elizabeth was just staring at Rose, trying to be polite in listening to her story. Rose could see that it was time to go home and made her excuses to her mum and dad, that the children needed to go to bed.

Back at the Mill, Rose put Roy Albert and Jim to bed. She went downstairs and noticed Arthur had changed out of his suit and was in his old clothes. He stoked the fire, "what a wonderful day Rose, I hope we have many more like it." This was the happiest Rose had ever seen Arthur. They both sat in their chairs watching the fire burn, feeling the warmth drawing from it. Rose told Arthur that she thinks Jim mentioned to May what he had heard in the car. Arthur was not too sure but Rose told him that the look May gave her said it all. "I don't want Jim causing trouble for us with May, mum, and dad. You know how he can stir things," Rose said.

Days had passed by, and Rose had avoided going to the Lawns to see her family just in case they confronted her with everything that has been happening lately. The payment for the next quarter was due and Rose had been busy preparing for this. Roy Albert and Jim were given their breakfast early, washed and dressed ready for the day ahead. Arthur left the house just after breakfast to attend to the livestock. Rose asked Jim to look after Roy Albert and to make sure he was kept clean. She went upstairs to make the beds when Jim decided to take Roy Albert into the garden to play. Rose called down to Jim, but there was no answer. Whilst rushing downstairs to see why there was no answer from Jim, there was a knock on the door. Rose turned towards the door and opened it, there stood a man in a smartly dressed suit and a bowler hat. Good morning, "I am looking for Rose Powell," he said, in a posh London accent. "Good morning," Rose replied. She looked over the gentleman's shoulder and could see Jim and Roy Albert sitting at the edge of the garden, playing in the puddles. She called to Jim, "come in and bring Edward with you, Jim looked puzzled, did she not mean Roy? The gentleman was asked into the house, with Jim and Roy Albert following. He noticed Edward's clothes were dirty; Rose explained straight away that this is normal when they had been playing outside. Rose asked the Palace rep his name, but he refused to give it, she had also noted that none of them would ever have a cup of tea during their visit. She thought this must be because of their professional role. The man handed Rose an envelope containing the money for Edward's welfare, and as he was leaving, he said, "I will report to the palace." Rose felt the report about Edward (Roy Albert) might not be a good one as he was on his own in the garden with Jim. Rose always tried to make sure the house was spotless, and Roy Albert was looking clean and tidy, so the Palace representatives did not have anything negative to say about them. Rose looked at Jim with rage in her face, he knew he was in trouble and went to his room.

# Chapter 40

# LET'S GET TO WORK

The following Thursday, an unexpected van turned up with a large crate for Rose. She called Arthur to deal with it, as she was changing Roy Albert. "What's this," Arthur asked. "We have driven down from London," the driver said. The other man in the van told Arthur that there was nothing to pay for the crate and where did he want us to leave it. Arthur asked them to leave the crate outside the front door. Rose thought it could only be from the Palace but did not understand why. They did not ask for anything when the representative was there just the week before. She asked Arthur to get something to open the large wooden crate. He used several tools to open it, including a screwdriver and a crowbar. Once Arthur managed to get the top of the crate off, they saw so many things inside. Rose could see the top of a sewing machine and let out a little squeal of excitement. She took out all that surrounded it. There was a square box inside, this was a sewing box, it contained so many different threads and needles. It had everything for sewing, fabric rolls were packed by the side of the machine, tweed fabric and cotton fabric, Rose got more and more excited, as she helped Arthur pull the rest of the crate apart, so they could lift out the sewing machine. "It's a Singer," Rose shrieked. It had a rounded lid it was pristine. They carried it into the house and placed it on the kitchen table. When everything else from the crate was in the house, Rose looked for a note of some kind saying where it was from, but there was nothing inside. She knew in her heart it must be from the Palace, but who would have sent such a wonderful gift. Rose wondered if she should write and thank them but remembered Mr Wigram had told her no contact is to be made.

Rose set out everything in the way that she wanted it to be and began making clothes for the boys straight away, using the incredible fabric. She made a pair of trousers for Arthur and two blouses out of the cotton fabric for herself. She loved looking at the different coloured cotton. Although she had sewn for many years, she had never had a full set of colours of such excellent quality.

Arthur came in for a cup of tea, saying that the cow and calf were doing well. Rose began telling Arthur about her new sewing machine, as she could do all these different stitches, and then there was a knock at the door. It was Frank, Arthur's brother. He had called to see how the farming was going. He started asking questions about how they could afford to do all these things, as everyone was talking about all this money they had. He would have like to know how they had earned it, as he could do with some himself. "What money?" Asked Rose. "Well, everyone is talking about you. You bought a cow and a calf from market, paid the deposit on this place, and look at what you have got there. All these new things, what did you do Arthur, rob a bank?" Rose thought Arthur was about to tell Frank everything, as she knew he had a job to be quiet about anything. Rose decided to make an excuse, "I was left some money by an aunt of mine, that's all. So, we thought we would spend some of it, but we can't spend any more of it, can we, Arthur! It's nearly all gone now." Arthur looked at Rose a little confused. Rose hinting to Arthur they needed to calm down on their spendings, Arthur agreed. Rose could not wait for Frank to leave so she could have a serious talk about being less extravagant with the money.

"No more spending, Arthur. No more boasting to people about you being a man of means. As you can see, everyone wants to know where we got the money. If it gets out, you know yourself the people in London will put a stop to it." Arthur knew Rose was right, but he liked the attention he was getting as he had a place in society, he did have a title. "But they all know I am Lord Glasbury, why shouldn't I show off a bit?" Rose understood what he was saying but told him that they could lose it all. She enjoyed the gifts and money and extras for the boys. She knew they had to be careful not to lose it because she was also pregnant again. At this point, she had not told anyone as she was going to wait until the time was right so continued with life as normal.

Rose took time out to sit and think, she began feeling more exhausted from being pregnant, looking after the children and helping on the farm. Whilst sitting quietly and thinking for a while her emotions would make her think of sad things in life, like when she was married to Fred. She did not have long enough with him to decide if it was a good marriage or not, due to his sudden death. She hated when he was ill all the time and was not overly upset when he passed away, as she had so many other things going on in her life at the time. She would also think of the Prince of Wales and her time with him, how he had broken her heart. She could not understand why she never felt the love for Fred like she loved the prince, and now there was Arthur. They did not get on at all well, there was no love between them, and if the money were not coming in, he would not be with her. Rose told Arthur when she was twelve weeks pregnant, he would be a father and he showed no emotion at all. She wondered if he would change when the baby came as it was his own child.

This is the 1934 sewing machine, still in the family today

# Chapter 41

# WHAT DID I SAY?

Each day rolled into the other, nothing exciting was happening as Rose waited for another letter from Jean. She would often think of Lewis, Jean, and herself laughing, chatting and making those lacy knickers. It now felt that working at the palace was the most wonderful time of her life. Rose picked up Roy and sat him on her lap. "Well, Edward. I am going to tell you about your father. He's a fine man, he lives in a big house and has plenty of money and mummy loved him very much. When you are old enough, I will tell you everything you need to know about him. Rose put Roy on the floor so he could toddle around, as she made a cup of tea for her and Arthur. "Arthur, I have made tea!" Rose called to him through the window, as he was looking over the gate at his cow. He never wanted to make conversation with anyone unless he had something to gain from it. He would answer if Rose asked him a question but would hardly continue with the discussion when Rose wanted to chat. She felt lonely and missed company. She wanted to chat about the Palace and everything in it, but she could not, all Arthur wanted to do was forget her past and except the money. Rose was getting bigger and feeling very uncomfortable. The baby was not due for several weeks, but she had discomfort and thought something could be wrong. She sent Arthur to fetch the nurse. On arrival the nurse came into the house and looked at Rose, after an examination, she told her she thought everything was all right and she needed to rest. The nurse told Rose that she was overdoing things as the baby was not due for another six weeks, and that rest for both herself and the baby was imperative. Later that evening Rose did not feel well as she sat on the chair. She suddenly felt sharp pains and knew things were not right. Arthur went to fetch Elizabeth, who helped Rose upstairs to her bedroom, as they both knew the baby was coming. It took several hours of pain before the baby was born and although Elizabeth thought the baby looked all right, he was very small. Rose lay in bed in a lot of pain and was dipping in and out of sleep as she felt exhausted. It was a different birth to the last two pregnancies where she felt drained after giving birth, but not ill like she felt at this moment. Elizabeth told her to rest while she cleaned the baby. She then helped Rose clean the blood-stained sheets from the bed which she replaced with clean ones. Elizabeth tucked him in his blanket and placed him next to Rose. By this time, it was now the early hours of the morning. Elizabeth took the sheets out to the tin bath, where Arthur had prepared some hot water. They soaked them in hot salt water to remove the blood. Arthur could see that Elizabeth was concerned for Rose, and he rushed upstairs to check on her and the baby. As he entered the bedroom he showed no emotion for the new baby boy, his concerns were for Rose as he could see she was not well.

That morning Rose had developed a fever and was tucked up in bed. Elizabeth stayed with her and dabbed her forehead with a cloth, as well as tending to the new-born baby 'Eric.' Rose began talking in her fever and was crying in a bad way. "I'm so sorry, he's dead." Rose cried. Elizabeth tried to reassure Rose that the baby was fine. "No, not the baby, the King. The King is dead." Rose continued. Elizabeth patted Rose on the shoulder, "Come on now, Rose. Snap out of it." Rose was delirious. The King had passed away that January and it was now April. As much as Rose was upset by the news of the King passing, she never told anyone how she felt at the time, and this was obviously playing on her mind. The Doctor arrived and examined Rose. He reassured Elizabeth and Arthur that what they were doing was helping Rose and as she was strong, the fever should soon break. Elizabeth continued sitting by Rose's side, dabbing her head with a cold flannel. Every time the flannel became warm, Elizabeth changed it for a colder one. Rose continued talking in her sleep, crying, and apologising for the King dying. Rose kept talking aloud, so Elizabeth spoke to reassure her that she was going to be all right, and she should not worry about the King. Rose began saying that the King would have been her father-in-law, if David, the Prince of Wales, had married her. Rose repeated, saying how much she loved him, and she knew he loved her back. Elizabeth hushed Rose telling her to rest and put a cold flannel on her head whilst holding her hand. Rose started to quieten down, then suddenly became hysterical and began screaming. Arthur rushed into the room, "is Rose alright," he said. Elizabeth looked at Arthur and said, "she has a temperature which is causing delirium, she was going to be alright." She asked Arthur if he could bring up some more cold water for her, once he had given the children their lunch.

Arthur broke off some bread and cheese and gave it to Jim and Roy. "Mummy wouldn't like you giving Roy bread and cheese," Jim remarked. Arthur looked around "what would she give him!" Arthur replied. Jim took a jar of stewed apple from the shelf. He passed it to Arthur and told him that "Roy has that for lunch with sugar on it." Arthur opened the jar of stewed apple and put some into a bowl with sugar and mixed it together before feeding it to Roy. As Jim was eating, he asked if his mummy was going to be up later. Arthur replied, "I don't know, she may need to stay in bed all day today." "Once you have had lunch you can go out to play in the garden with Roy." Jim disagreed, "no he has to be changed and go to bed for his afternoon nap." Arthur refused, saying he was not doing that and went upstairs with some cold water for Rose. He asked Elizabeth if she would change Roy's nappy and put him to bed. Elizabeth did not want to leave Rose alone, so asked Arthur to continue putting a cold flannel on her forehead.

Arthur gently patted her head with it to cool her down. Rose began crying in her sleep again as Arthur told her everything was going to be all right. She started calling out for David and saying how sorry she was for her behaviour and that she loved him and begged for his forgiveness. Arthur sat there not knowing what to do or say as he kept the cold compress on her forehead. Elizabeth on returning to the bedroom could hear Rose calling out, suggesting that there had not been any improvement in her condition. Arthur asked Elizabeth "do you think Rose would love me, as much as she loved David, now we have a child of our own." She reminded Arthur, "that you needed to show love to Rose, and forget that you married her for the money." Arthur did not deny this, he did tell her how he liked being with Rose before she went to London. He said that "I had hoped that one day Rose would have feelings for me, together we could be good friends," but he could not see that happening soon. "Are you going to leave Rose with the three children or are you going to stay and make this farm pay?" Elizabeth asked him openly. Arthur did not hesitate to reassure Elizabeth that he was going to stay as he knew Rose would not be able to cope on her own. Elizabeth placed her hand on his shoulder, she stood up and said, "I will go and check on Roy and Jim, and I'll make Eric a bottle of milk." A brief time later, Elizabeth came up the stairs and into the bedroom, Arthur was nodding off in the chair, and Rose was still fighting her demons, crying, and talking in her sleep. Elizabeth hated seeing her daughter in such an unwell state, having to go through all this pain.

After feeding Eric, Elizabeth sat beside Rose and rested her head on the side of the bed, she softly closed her eyes to rest them. Next thing, she was suddenly awakened by screams and crying from Eric. Rose was still in a deep sleep and Arthur had not stirred, still fast asleep in the chair. Elizabeth picked up Eric and gave him a cuddle to calm him, then took him downstairs to make up a bottle of milk for him. She could hear Roy wandering around his bedroom. Elizabeth brought Roy into the bedroom with her and Eric, she laid Eric into the bottom draw of the dresser hoping he would now settle. Roy wanted to climb into bed with his mummy, but Elizabeth told him "He must not, as mummy was still sleeping, she wasn't feeling well," and then with a screeching cry Roy woke his mum. Rose looked puzzled at Roy and her mother, asking her mother what time it was, as she tried to remember what had happened. Elizabeth explained to Rose everything she had gone through that night and assured her that baby Eric was fine.

Elizabeth awoke Arthur, "Arthur go down and light the fire ready to make breakfast." "I will bring Roy down once I have changed him," she said. Jim and Roy had boiled eggs and soldiers for breakfast with Arthur. Elizabeth took Rose up a cup of sweet tea, hoping this would perk her up a bit. "Rose I will be heading home soon to check on your father and May," Rose begged her mother not to go. Elizabeth told Rose she would stay a while longer, to make sure Jim went to school, and that Arthur was helping with Roy and Eric. She went on to say what Rose had said in her sleep, in front of Arthur. At that moment into the bedroom came Arthur with Roy. Elizabeth tried to convince Rose and Arthur that it was the fever that made her say those things, but Rose confessed that those words and feelings were true. Arthur left Roy with Rose as he said, "I will see Jim to School and then I have to pick up some things for the farm." After Arthur had left the room, Rose explained to Elizabeth that she would never love Arthur as she had given her heart away to David. "You got it back after Fred had died," Elizabeth replied, but Rose said that she never loved Fred like she loved David. She told her mother that when Fred died, she never felt as much pain in her heart as she did when David pushed her away, even though the Prince of Wales was not dead, he just destroyed her. Elizabeth found that hard to listen to. "Right, my girl, you listen to me, you put on a brave face, and you look after your family. No more fancy dreams. That prince did not love you. He only wanted one thing and when he got it, this is the result as she looked at Roy. You let that go, and get on with the life you have, or you will end up with nothing." Elizabeth went downstairs. Rose lay further back into her pillow cuddling Roy. She needed to rest and drifted off to sleep.

When Rose awoke, she could smell the food cooking. She wondered who was downstairs knowing full well that Arthur could not boil water. Mrs Brooks from the neighbouring farm was there to help the family. She had heard what had been happening at the Mill, and brought over some freshly cooked food for Rose, Arthur, and family. She made sure they were fed that day and the next day. Rose called down for Arthur, Mrs Brooks went upstairs to see Rose and could see how unwell she looked. "I will come every day until you feel fit enough to get out of bed," She assured Rose. Rose was incredibly grateful and tearfully thanked Mrs Brooks for everything. Roy was up running around so Mrs Brooks took him and Eric down to Arthur, she then warmed a bottle of milk and passed it to Arthur to feed the baby. This was the first time Arthur had fed a new-born, so she showed him how to hold the baby in one arm and placed the bottle in Eric's mouth. "Not too high or he will get wind in his belly and that will give him colic, we don't want that," Mrs Brooks remarked. She was a big thick-set woman, a true farmer's wife, and would take no messing, making sure that Arthur learnt how to do things to help with their children. Mrs Brooks watched Arthur for a few moments as he was feeding Eric, when she was happy that he was doing it right, she told him that she would be off home. "I will return tomorrow morning with lunch for you all, Arthur you will have to make breakfast," Mrs Brooks said. As soon as Mrs Brooks left Arthur took Eric upstairs to see Rose. He thought, as Rose was led down, she would be able to feed Eric. He could see Rose was fast asleep, so he turned around heading towards the door and Eric began to cry. He could see Rose wake up. "Can you feed him, and keep an eye on Roy, I need to go and check on the cows." Rose lifted herself up and took Eric in her arms, held him close to her chest and fed him with the bottle. She comforted him, holding him for what felt like an eternity, as she had barely touched or even seen her new-born baby since she gave birth to him. Eric began dosing off as Rose gently rocked him to sleep. Little footsteps came rushing upstairs and just by the corner of the bedroom door, Rose could see Roy hiding to the side of it. "You will have to climb up onto the bed yourself if you want to get in. I can't lift you up." Roy's eyes lit up as he ran over to the bed. He tried climbing up but could not get himself onto the bed and lifted his arms out for his mother, "uppy, uppy," Roy shouted, to pull him up, but she could not. She kept telling him to try and get himself up, but he became upset and started crying. Jim just home from school, came up the stairs and saw his younger brother crying, and lifted him onto the bed to sit by his mummy and baby brother. Rose stopped Jim as he was leaving the room, "Where's your dad?" Jim turned to face his mother, "Still dead! But Arthur is outside. "he's not helping you with Roy and Eric is he mum. He is a lazy shit." Rose raised her voice, wanting to give Jim a slap for his rudeness but it hurt when she began moving forward, so collapsed back into her pillow. "You do not speak about him like that, it's not very nice." Jim had a grumpy expression on his face with his arms crossed, "Well, he is. He makes excuses for everything. The only thing he does love is his cows." He then went on to say, "do you need a nappy or some clothes for Eric!" Rose told him she would let him sleep for the moment and change him with his next feed, but she did ask him to look after Roy as a big brother should.

**Arthur with Roy at his side and Eric in his arm**

# Chapter 42

## LIVING WITHIN YOUR MEANS

It took several days before Rose began feeling well enough to get out of bed and look after the children. Thanks to the kindness of Mrs Brooks, the children and Arthur were well fed. Rose found it hard work to keep on top of everything, looking after the children, feed and change Eric, and Roy constantly needing attention. Jim helped his mum when he was home from school, and Arthur could have helped a lot more, but he would always have an excuse not to have to be there. Arthur saw this kind of housework only suitable for Rose. It was women's work and therefore she should do it without any assistance from him. On the other hand, when Rose was well, Arthur would expect Rose to milk the cows, feed the chickens and attend the vegetable patch in the garden.

Wednesday was closing in, and Arthur wanted to go to market to buy some spring lambs. He spoke to Rose and explained why he wanted them, she thought it would be a good idea as they could breed from them the following year and make some money. She loved it when Arthur was cheerful working on the farm with his ideas of improvement, than her disagreeing with him and him being miserable. With the help from Jim watching over his little brothers, Rose had the chance to take in alterations for people around the area. She would never miss an opportunity of making a little extra money. Rose was an excellent seamstress and always did a perfect job, putting in every bit of detail and attention to each piece of fabric she touched.

As soon as the fruit and vegetables were ready for picking, Rose would preserve as many as possible. She would place layers and layers of salt between the vegetables to preserve them for the winter. She would boil the fruit and add the sugar to make jars of jam and store them in her pantry. Rose enjoyed looking at the shelves packed full, from one end to the other they were lined up with jars of different jam's that she had made. She knew this would help feed her family through the winter months. Rose was gifted with her hands at making things to help either feed the family or keep them warm and comfortable. Making patchwork quilts and cushions or using long pieces of fabric and turning them together into rag mats. If the house ever became cold, Rose would always make something new to keep them all warm. She would go out into the fields looking for sheep's wool; where the sheep had rubbed themselves around the edges of the field, they would leave small amounts of wool from their fleece. Rose would collect as much as she could possibly find and wash and card it, to make it into felt or knit it into a pullover for Arthur.

The summer months made Rose feel great in herself. The hot sun warming her cheeks as she would spend most of her day outside. Even though it was hot, she would still always need to light the fire as this was the only way for her to boil water and cook. The windows would always be open during the summer months, sometimes until late at night so the kitchen did not overheat with the burning fire. Early morning sunrise and a late sunset kept her smiling, and her troubles would seem to disappear for a moment. She enjoyed listening to the birds singing and although she was not a religious woman, she would thank the lord for days like these. Arthur hung his shaving mirror on the nail which he had knocked into the window frame, so it was at the right height for him. He had covered his face with shaving soap, Rose walked behind him and slid her arms around his waist, causing Arthur to jump and he nicked his face. The blood started to trickle down his cheek, "Can't you see I am shaving? You made me cut myself." Rose did not care as she was feeling happy and playful, but Arthur was not in the mood and told her to behave herself. "I need to shave and brush my hair ready for market." Rose let go of him and went to make breakfast, eggs and soldiers, their favourite. Eric was now old enough to have some egg. Rose put a small amount in his mouth, and he played with it for a while. She could see him moving it back and forth and then he spat it out. Jim and Roy found that hilarious and were laughing and giggling at him. Rose gave him a little more egg, this time it was mashed. He did the same thing again, so Rose gave him his bottle. Once the breakfast was finished and the table was cleared away, Rose put Eric down for his nap. The boys would go outside and play in the garden, and Rose would take a walk to check on the vegetables growing. Arthur was walking across to the far field looking at his cows and sheep along the way and making sure they had drinking water in the tanks. He would often take his gun with him to shoot some rabbits. Then the rabbits would be hung up in the outside shed, ready for Rose to prepare. Rose knew she had to dress them as soon as possible as flies would be attracted to them and lay eggs on them. Once they had maggots, Rose would not want to use them.

Roy enjoyed helping his mum with the rabbits and watched her dress them (Dressing - Removing the skin and innards of the rabbit). As a three-year-old boy, Roy would ask all sorts of questions to his mummy. Rose would explain that the rabbits were food and that did not worry him as he smoothed them. She was waiting for the next Wednesday to come, she would go to the butchers and buy lamb, until then rabbit was a delicious meal for them. Rose and Roy took the dressed rabbits into the house and placed them into the sink full of salt water to soak. Rose gave Roy and Jim a drink and a biscuit before they ran back outside to play.

Later that afternoon, Roy came running in with blood on his face, both Rose and Arthur looked him all over but could not find a scratch on him. Rose called Jim in, worried he may have been hurt instead. He came in with blood covered hands. Rose shrieked with fear, "What have you been doing?" Jim lowered his head, "I'm trying to bury the rabbit heads." He sheepishly replied. Rose and Arthur looked at one another. Jim continued explaining, "I took Roy outside to play and he went into the shed. When I went in, he was holding the rabbits' ears. He had them against his head shouting, bunny, bunny, so I took them and tried to bury them with the rubbish at the bottom of the garden." Rose could see Jim was trying to keep Roy out of mischief and said, "we were worried something bad had happened when we saw blood on you both." Jim went to wash his hands to clean off the blood and Rose took the flannel and scrubbed Roy's face, chuckling at the thought of him holding the ears shouting, bunny, bunny. Arthur, Roy, and Jim went back outside as Rose went upstairs to check on Eric.

She could see Arthur and the two boys going further into the field and went to get her fur coat out from under the bed. She reached under the bed and pulled out the box. It was covered thick with dust as she had not checked on it in such a long time. She brushed off the dust and removed the lid, pulling out the coat, it did not smell as fresh as it once did, as she had not aired it in so long. Standing up she tried on the coat to see if it still fitted. With the coat on, it transported her mind back to London all those years ago, in the prince's room with his arms around her waist. She swayed slowly side to side and could hear his voice calling her wosey posey and having his chin rubbing against her neck. She stopped every few moments as she remembered little bits of detail that opened her memories. She could smell his cologne that was mixed with a bit of smoke. She remembered the time he had a cigarette in his mouth and how the smoke blew across his face making him close one eye, this reminded Rose of Popeye the Sailor Man. The memories Rose were reminiscing was interrupted abruptly when Arthur came into the house shouting for Rose. She did not hear what he said, but knew she had to quickly get out of the coat and put it away. With the heat of the weather and having that long fur coat on, Rose struggled to get it off in time before Arthur was up the stairs and standing in the room before her. A brief silence between Rose and Arthur was broken when Arthur told Rose to get the coat off. "What the bloody hell are you doing? Do you know where Roy was? "Yes, with you," Rose replied. Arthur then shouted, "he was close to the fire and nearly burnt himself while you were playing dress up." Give me that bloody coat, I am going to burn it." He lunged forward to grab the coat, but Rose was quicker at pulling it away from his reach. Arthur stormed downstairs leaving Rose holding her fur coat tight. Rose quickly put the coat back in the box and kicked it under the bed and went downstairs to check on Roy.

Roy was playing in front of the fire, gazing at the flames, calling them pretty. He would not listen to his mother when she said he must not touch the fire as he would get burnt. She picked him up and asked Jim to take him into the garden to play, while she prepared tea. Rose knew Arthur was angry but did not want to fight, so left him out in the shed banging around. Jim came in and asked what Arthur was doing as he was making so much noise outside. "He's got some chicken wire and wooden rails and he's making a pen for the chickens," Rose explained. Rose wondered why they needed a new chicken run, but if that is what Arthur was doing, that was up to him.

After tea Rose continued with her daily household chores, she had all the washing on the line and would need to get it in. She then took the rugs out and hung them on the line to beat them with a brush. She could not believe the cloud of dust that bounced off with every beat, as she cleaned them on a regular basis. The banging in the shed had stopped, Arthur came out and asked Rose if she could make him a cup of tea. She went into the house to make a pot of tea as she did not want any ill feelings between them, in front of the children. The behaviour of Arthur was one that confused Rose most of the time, especially if something had happened to upset him as she never knew his true feelings. After he finished his cup of tea, Arthur went back to the shed and the banging continued for a little longer until it was silent again.

The shed door swung open and out came Arthur, carrying this large wooden frame with chicken wire around it. Rose could not help but wonder where he was going to put it, as he passed by her into the house and took it into the sitting room. He opened it out to what looked like a large clothes horse, three pieces of wood hinged together, they formed a triangle. It had a hook either side to attach it to the wall. Rose understood the idea Arthur had, to keep the children safe from the fire, but when it was opened and attached to the wall, it had a point sticking out at the front. Rose did not know how to tell Arthur it was no good without getting into a full heated argument. Arthur stood back and looked to Rose for a response, but she just looked and gave a slight uncomfortable grin. Arthur began chuckling to himself before laughing aloud. Rose thought he had gone mad. "It's rubbish, I know what I have done, I have forgotten the other side, it's supposed to be a box shape, not a triangle." He unhooked the sides and took it back outside to the shed, much to the relief of Rose. An hour later, Arthur came back in with the new and improved version of his fire guard to protect the boys. He must have taken it all apart as it was a little shorter but had four pieces, it fitted perfectly. It was enough to keep the boys away from the fire, so they did not hurt themselves and it was short enough for Rose to reach over and build up the fire when she needed to.

# Chapter 43

# THE ABDICATION

That evening, after the children went to bed, Rose and Arthur were sat by the fire, something they did most nights. Silently sitting with only the sound of the fire crackling and roaring to stop it from being an uneasy, awkward silence. This evening was different though. Arthur chuckled every time Rose attended to the fire to keep it burning. Rose did not understand why he chuckled, but it was an improvement and thought better things were to come.

The next morning, after the chores were all done, the house was cleaned and the boys were washed and dressed, and Jim went off to school, there was a knock at the door. Rose looked through the window to see who was knocking the door, it was Frank. "Have you read about the abdication of our new King?" he asked. Rose did not have time to respond before Frank entered the house and continued, "King Edward had finally done it and abdicated." Frank explained that he had heard it on the wireless at the farm down the road. The farm down the road had electricity and they had invited anyone that wanted to listen. Rose looked at Arthur, "Did you know about this?" Arthur looked to the ground and said nothing. Rose was disappointed and upset, "Why didn't you tell me? I would have wanted to hear that; you know I would have." Frank stepped in to defend his brother, "Now, you hang on a minute Rose, it was only a speech. It's sad what he has done, running off with a woman of that nature and giving up his country and all that, but there's no need to get this upset. It isn't as though you knew him personally." Rose looked to Arthur to see if he could step in and say something, but he did not. So, with a puffed-out face with anger, Rose stormed out of the room and went upstairs to be alone. She would hear Frank harping on and on, about what a fool the King was and what kind of woman Wallis Simpson would be. Rose was hoping, with each comment Frank made, that Arthur would tell him to go home but his voice remained downstairs babbling on in the kitchen. Rose knew she could not remain upstairs all day as Frank wouldn't leave if it was just up to Arthur, so she pulled herself together and with a deep breath, returned downstairs to the kitchen, ignoring both Frank and Arthur. Frank looked at Rose as she brushed past them both. "Well, I am sorry if I have upset you, Rose. I can't understand you. Everyone else who has spoken of this, agreed he was a fool to leave this country for her, but no one is as upset as you. I know you worked in London, but it's not as though you knew him personally, is it?" Once again, Rose looked at Arthur to see if he would speak up for his wife, but his lips were closed. "Right. If you're not doing anything in here, go outside and find something to do, or better still Frank, bugger off back home and let Arthur get on with his work." Frank knew that Rose would continue moaning at them all day if he stayed, so said his goodbyes to the family and left.

As Arthur went outside to his shed, Rose started to prepare a stew for dinner. She had a couple of pheasants that needed cooking, she plucked and dressed, and decided to boil them, adding onions, leeks, carrots, and a cabbage. She added dried pearl barley and some dried peas and let this boil for hours until the meat fell off the bones. Rose took out the meat and bones and strained the liquid into another pan, sifted through everything, making sure no hard bits were left so the children could not choke on it. The veg was practically mashed and the barley was soft. Bit by bit, she added nearly everything back to the pot. keeping back any bones and skin from the meat. Adding the original liquid and set it back on the fire to cook. She knew there would be plenty of it to eat over the coming days. Each day she could add something extra to stretch the meal out that little longer. Rose knew they were lucky on the whole. With the money coming for Roy and everything they had, Rose was most grateful. Though when she spoke to Arthur, he always wanted that little bit more. More cows, more land, and a bigger house with more rooms. It was always want, want, want with him. Sometimes, Rose wondered if Arthur would ever be satisfied. The only thing Rose ever truly wanted was the love of the prince, and this she knew, she would never have. Rose knew if she had a spare five minutes, she would often daydream about what might have been rather than what actually was. She could be living in a palace or just in London. Shopping or dining at some fancy restaurant with glamorous friends, drinking cocktails in the evening, and then some noise or another thing would soon bring her back to reality.

Rose would often think of the families around her, not many were making money, and living to the standard she wanted to live. She wanted a London lifestyle but on the farm. The neighbouring farm was a large farm, and although they made money, they never lived above their means, Mrs Brooks always made do. Very rarely would they buy anything new. It had to be worn out or completely non-repairable before she would buy something they needed. The Mill had cows they could milk, and they could make butter, not enough to sell as a business but enough to feed the family. Rose still did alterations for the locals and that brought in a few shillings from time to time.

The day was flying by, Rose was catching up with the rest of her chores. Then she remembered that she had not put her fur coat away properly when she took it out a few days before. She checked to make sure the children were settled and asked Jim to look after Roy. Ensuring the guard was in front of the fire so that the children could not touch it she made her way upstairs. She pulled out the box from under the bed and took out the crumpled coat, giving it a firm shake as she could, she made sure that it was flat and stretched out properly. She felt the small ring box in the pocket. The emerald ring that the Prince of Wales gave her all those years ago was still in there. She took the ring out the box and tried it on each finger, it still would not fit. The cardboard box that the coat came in was now falling apart and needed some attention. Rose noticed a small amount of mould on the outside of the box which had been caused by the damp in and around the house. She knew that having it tucked away in a box under the bed was not the best place for it, but where else could she store it, knowing it would upset Arthur. Rose realised she had to do something to save the coat and ring box from being completely destroyed, so went downstairs into the kitchen to find some string. As she made her way into the kitchen, she could see the boys playing together, she took a ball of string and the scissors from the drawer and took them back upstairs. She tied up the box with the string, but she did not slide it back under Jim's bed, she took the box to her own bedroom and placed it safely in her wardrobe. Ensuring there was something under the box to keep it off the bottom of the wardrobe so it would not get damp. Rose placed some old blankets on top of the box to hide it, in case Arthur opened the wardrobe. Each time she put the coat away it was a constant reminder of the love she had for the prince.

Arthur came home, wet, and cold, moaning that one of the yearlings was stuck in the hedge. He had to pull it out which made him fall backwards causing him to roll down the bank and into the stream. Rose told him she would boil the water for him to have a bath and change his clothes, as he could catch a cold. Arthur refused to take a bath, he dried himself off by the fire and Rose fetched him a change of clothes.

# Chapter 44

# THAT'S LIFE

The seasons at the farm passed quickly. Married to Arthur and with the children growing up so fast, mum would say, "watching a child grow happens so fast, but with a few children, it feels like the speed of light. You look at them as they grow, and then realise the younger one is now at the age his older brothers once were."

Rose's father passed away; the whole family were heartbroken. May and Elizabeth continued living and working at the Lawns, Arthur would offer to help with the fencing and sheering when it was needed. Rose was pregnant again and soon due to give birth. She grew in size very quickly at an early stage of pregnancy and found it more difficult to do things. Jim was worried about his Aunty May now that his granddad had died and wanted to help her as much as possible. Rose was concerned about having a fever again, like she did when she gave birth to Eric.

When it was time to give birth, the Nurse was ready and so was Elizabeth. The labour took several hours for Rose, when the baby was welcomed to the world, it was a boy. He was the largest of them all, nearly ten pounds in weight. Eric was not much heavier than that, when he was three months old. It took them a while to think of a name. It changed so many times from Thomas, to Albert, then Arthur would suggest a name, but Rose did not like it. Elizabeth would also say the name of someone who she knew, usually associated with an older man. They eventually settled on a name, "John." He had a mop of red hair the same as Jim, and he had green eyes. Rose could not help but look at the differences and similarities of each of the children. Jim had similar looks to his father, Fred, the same hair, and eye colour. Eric had dark hair and dark eyes, and then she looked at Roy who was still with his yellow, blonde hair, and blue-green eyes. Roy was also getting chubby and stood out like a sore thumb. The more he grew, his facial features were developing, he looked different from his brothers. Rose thought of dying his hair and rubbed mud on it for several days to try and darken it, but there was nothing she could do about his face shape or eye colour. The other boys had oval shaped faces like Arthur and his brothers, while Roy looked fat and rounded. Rose thought that his face shape might change as he got older and would lose the chubby features. She once heard that all children would eventually grow to look alike.

The newest member of the family, John, was a good baby. Everything as regular as clockwork. Rose noticed that he drunk more milk at feed time, than his brothers did when they were babies. John was a good sleeper which helped Rose get on with her work around the farm. She never felt the need to cuddle the boys, she wanted them to be brought up strong and hard, not soppy, and soft. Rose could not remember the last time she had cuddled Jim or even given him any praise and it did not seem to do him any harm. Roy on the other hand, needed picking up, carrying around, and sitting on her lap for much longer. Eric only ever had attention when he needed something such as, changing or feeding. When Eric needed food, Jim or Roy would feed him. That seemed to work for Rose, and it was only on an odd occasion when Arthur would get involved with the children. His idea was that Rose had them so she should look after them, nothing would change his mind on that. This is what a woman was for, that kind of work, and no real man would ever think to do it.

The next morning the postman arrived with a letter from Jean. Rose was excited to receive a letter from her friend, as it would keep her updated on what has been happening at York House and the Palace. The letter mentioned that Jean thought Mrs Gray had a slight crush on Mr Williams, and how funny it was to see them having long glance's towards one another. The letter also revealed on one occasion, in the kitchen, Mr Williams touched Mrs Gray on the hand while passing the cruet, and held it there for longer than was necessary, this made Mrs Gray blush red. It also explained that their friend Lewis, had not met anyone else, she was still eating all the leftovers, and getting wider by the week. She had had three larger uniforms since Rose had left and Mrs Gray was quite concerned. Page had left employment and had married her fiancé, she had no plans to return to the palace, as he had an excellent job, and they were hoping to start a family. The letter then went on to talk about what had been happening with Jean. She was still walking out with Samual he was a fine upstanding gentleman, whom she had met, when Rose worked there. The rest of the letter was asking of Rose and her family. Rose sat down after reading the letter, wishing how she could see Jean and Lewis. More Jean than Lewis as she always found Lewis a bit more difficult to have a good relationship with, she looked at life differently and was not afraid to say so.

Arthur came home for lunch, Rose showed him she had received another letter from Jean, but he did not really want to hear Rose going on about London. It made him feel insecure and knew it would leave Rose all over the place with her feelings. He thought she would just settle into a quiet life with him and the four boys. Arthur was helping Elizabeth and May at the Lawns, this kept him away from the farm a lot more than usual. Rose did not mind this as looking after the children and conducting her chores kept her occupied. She decided that the next time she went shopping in Hereford she would buy some embroidery silks, to make a small embroidery to hang on the wall. She kept thinking about the huge tapestries at the Palace, how much time and hard work it had taken to make them. There were times, especially after receiving a letter, she did anything else but think of the Palace and York House and dreamt of wanting to run away back to London. She looked around the house she was living in now, and it brought her back to reality.

The money still came from the Palace every quarter. The reps, as Rose called them, had changed a lot, some had an attitude towards her. They would give her a look of disgust, and she could see them judging her. Others would smile and ask if all was all right with Edward (Roy Albert). They would sometimes ask his age and of his health. One of the rep's who visited the house had written a list of questions. He asked Rose about the child's speech, if he ate well, and did he sleep good at nights. She found this strange as the others were not so interested in him. Rose asked him if he had children of his own, he told her he had two. He could see that Edward was a healthy young boy, bright and cheerful. He told Rose he would report to the palace that all was well, and he then handed Rose an envelope and headed for the door. She still had not told them that she changed Edward's name to Roy Albert, and she noticed that this rep did not ask if Edward needed anything. Rose did not query it as she was grateful to receive the money.

Arthur kept in touch with Mr Wigram, he would often telephone him. Mr Wigram was not the Kings private secretary anymore, although he still held a position within the Royal Household. He liked Arthur, not at first, but just like a fine wine, Arthur got better with age. Mr Wigram would inquire about Arthur, the farm, and the boy. Arthur would ask how Mr Wigram was keeping, but neither party ever mentioned the Prince of Wales in their conversation. Mr Wigram had also written to Rose and Arthur and in one letter, he had written that both the King, and Queen, had asked most tenderly about the boy. This pleased Rose more than any other letter she had received, as they had enquired about the boy, her boy, their grandson. She felt this was recognition not only that he existed, but he was something to do with them. They had never denied that. After King George had passed away and the payments kept coming, Rose had convinced herself that it must have been Queen Mary who was paying for Roy; as David, her prince, a King for only one year, had moved on, he would not give Rose or Arthur acknowledgement of any sort, let alone pay for a child he did not want to know.

Now King George VI was married and had children of his own, Rose did not think he would be prepared to pay for Edward the son of his brother. Rose wondered if he ever knew Roy existed. She would think of all different people who would be the one to send the money. At one point, she thought it may have been Mr Wigram himself but then on the other hand, she thought to herself why he would pay for Roy. It was not his problem or responsibility. So, Rose would go back to her first thought that it had to be Queen Mary.

Rose was looking out of the window at Arthur, wondering what stupid thing he may possibly do this week. He would do things other people would not think of doing. She could see him climbing up a tree with a handsaw and attempting to saw off the overhanging branch. She could not believe her eyes when she went outside. He was sitting on the end of the branch. If it had snapped under his weight, he would have fallen twenty feet to the ground. Rose quickly ran over to the tree to ask Arthur what he was doing. She could see he did not realise as he scurried back towards the tree itself. Rose shook her head in disbelief that someone could be that senseless, she moved the children, who were also playing near the tree, inside the house for their safety. Rose kept an eye on Arthur from the window, as he sawed the branch, and then it came crashing down in the place where the boys were sat moments before. Arthur carefully climbed down from the tree, he moved the branch to the side of the garden so it could dry out and be used as wood for the fire. Rose felt she had made a big mistake marrying Arthur, but she could do nothing about it. She tried to make the best of things for her and the children but found it challenging work, especially when he would do silly things that annoyed her.

# Chapter 45

# THE BEGINNING OF WORLD WAR 2

In early 1939 the talk of war was everywhere. It had been on the minds of many people, but now it seemed closer than ever. Rose was petrified as she had heard so many stories of the great war that had happened just two decades before. She spoke to her mother about it, Elizabeth told her to go to town and stock up on everything she could afford, as things would become tight. Rose spoke to Arthur about it, and he thought she was worrying over nothing. On that Wednesday they were in the market, Rose began to buy what she could to stock her pantry. She bought more dry goods than normal, flour, pearl barley and dried peas. She enjoyed keeping her pantry full. It was already stocked with the jams and salted vegetables from the garden, but Rose felt she needed more.

Over the following few weeks and months, Rose was buying more and more to stock up but the shelves in stores and on the markets were getting emptier and emptier as everyone across the country were doing the same and the British Prime Minister, Neville Chamberlain, was preparing the UK for what was likely to come. In April 1939 every young British man at the age of 20 and 21 who were fit and able, had to do six months of military training.

September 3rd, 1939, Great Britain, and France declared war on Germany for their invasion of Poland. The people of the UK did not know if the fighting was going to reach them as they were far away from Germany. The British Army did not have as many young men in their forces as the French did and so the government made all abled men between 18 and 41 would be liable for conscription. It was also declared that single men would be called to war before married men. Men aged 20-23 were required to register on the 21st of October 1939. The age of registration was increasing over time for as many men to join the fight for King and country. Rose was thankful her boys were too young to fight and with Arthur being a farmer, did not have to go to war. Rose and Arthur executed as normal and helped do their part by supporting the other families in their area of Hereford who had to say goodbye to their brothers, sons, fathers, and husbands.

The main part of Hereford was the munitions factory, Royal Ordnance Factory (ROF 4) or Rotherwas, as it was known as in World War one. This was primarily operated by women who had taken up a lot of the men's jobs as they went to fight overseas. There was a campaign for everyone to donate any spare kitchen pots so they could be melted down. Rose sorted out her pans, she did not have many but found two to donate. Arthur took them to the collection depot in Hereford. There was talk of a home guard and with no age limit, this was for anyone who wished to join. They had weekly meetings and were told who and what to look out for if they saw the enemy. Farmers were told they could use their own shotgun if needed. Arthur was not one of the Home Guards who was required to patrol Hereford, that job was for the men of the city. He and his surrounding neighbours would have a plan of what to do if there were any signs of trouble. Although Hereford was a market town and had the munitions factory, it was evident that it would play a big part in the war, it could be a target, so the people of Hereford took their patrols seriously. Rose had to fill out the forms to apply for the ration books. It was for Arthur, Rose and all the children. They had coupons for food and then for clothing and shoes. Rose couldn't believe what each family was supposed to live on, she was more than grateful that they had fresh milk from the cows each day. Butter and soft cheeses were made each week from the milk. They had their vegetables growing in the garden, although not much was growing at that time of year. They had a few cabbages left which Rose made sure were not wasted. They were allowed bacon on rations which Rose found useful as they had their own eggs. Anything Arthur could catch in the fields, such as rabbits and wild birds could also be added to a stew, although there were not that many of them around. This was because other farmers were doing the same to survive. Rose would prepare the occasional old hen or cockerel to eat, but there was never a lot of meat on them. As the war went on, times were becoming more difficult for the family. The boys were growing, eating a lot more food, it became a challenge for Rose to put food on the table.

Operation Pied Piper was underway across the country, as the government were worried that the larger towns and cities would get bombed. Notices were put up asking people to offer their homes and take in evacuee children. People were compelled to take in the evacuee, and they may receive a fine if they declined. Homes that were host to the evacuees would be given payments for the number of children they took in. Arthur thought this would be a good idea, having a few extra children wouldn't make much difference to him. Rose on the other hand, was not liking the idea. They did not have enough room for her, Arthur, and the boys, let alone having to take in more children. Mrs Brooks took in several evacuees, she had children from all over Great Britain. Their farm had several unused bedrooms and electricity. Although she was very regimented with her way of living, she was good with the children and the rations. She made clothes for them as they hardly had anything with them when they arrived at the farm. Mrs Brooks would knit hats and gloves to keep the children warm or she would be lining their thin little coats. Anything to make these city children warm and comfortable in the open countryside. Some days, you would see her and the children walking the lanes, like a brood of chicks, as she taught them the names of different trees and showed them the cattle and sheep. Most of the children had never seen animals of this nature and one or two of the children had never patted a dog. The difference between lives in the city and lives in the country was becoming more realistic. The city children could not name any of the vegetables which Mrs Brooks found really sad. She would walk the children to the Mill Farm to see Rose, and the children would play with Roy and Eric. There was a small child who stood out from all the rest. The children would often touch his face or feel his hair. None of the other children had ever seen a person who looked like him. It was in fact the first time Mrs Brooks and Rose had ever seen someone with dark skin. He was a lovely little boy, and everyone liked him. Mrs Brooks said she treated them all the same, but she was often seen cuddling him more. She loved the children and was sad to see them leave. They were leaving at different times during the war which the other children also found sad as they grew strong bonds, they didn't know if they would ever see them again. Occasionally there would be a new face that would join the family of evacuees Mrs Brooks took in.

# Chapter 46

# THE WAR AT HOME

Monday 27th July 1942, the quiet countryside air was broken by the sound of an aeroplane engine, far in the distance, before an air raid siren screamed through the wind. You could hear it for miles. A single German Dornier Do17, twin-engine, medium range bomber, opened its bomb hatch and dropped two bombs. One bomb fell, whistling as it came hurtling down to earth, landing on the Royal Ordnance Factory. It pierced through the roof of the transit shed before exploding, killing 17 people, and injuring many more. Moments later a second bomb bounced over the perimeter fence of the factory and landed on a house just over the other side. It exploded, tearing through the house, killing five members of one family, leaving just one survivor. Rose was scared to hear the news of the bombing in Hereford, so close to home. Arthur kept trying to convince Rose that they were safe on the farm.

During the war, Rose became pregnant again with her fifth child, Alfred, known as Fred. She believed things would be different this time, as people were becoming more and more anxious and struggling with the rationing. Rose and Arthur would head into Hereford for supplies, speaking to the shopkeepers, they would hear the horror stories of how the British soldiers had died. Rose would go home and cry, she was heartbroken to hear these stories. Elizabeth was also sad to hear the news reports of war. It was only her and May at the

Lawns, she found it hard to get around as she was now in her late seventies.

Arthur helped at the Lawns as much as he could. Rose was becoming more and more afraid of the war as time went on. The boys were getting older, and there was no sign of the war ending. Although Arthur assisted Elizabeth and May he knew his work priority had to be at home. May was finding things financially tight as she was not taking in any extra work, like she had previously done with her father. The war brought a lot of women to the larger farms around the country, these women were known as the Land Girls. They would help plough, plant, and harvest the crops for the farmers. May and Elizabeth required help at the Lawns, they could not afford to pay one of the Land Girls as the farm was quite small, Jim would help May on the land as much as he could.

In town everyone had to stand in long lines outside the stores, waiting to use their coupons. They would chat and sing to each other to keep their spirits up. Arthur was always trying to remain positive about the war. He would reassure Rose that everything was going to be fine, until he saw a young man with a leg missing being helped into the pub by his father. This was distressing for him to see and made him question the part he was playing to help win the war.

Arthur rang Mr Wigram as he had heard the King and Queen were staying at Buckingham Palace. He offered vegetables or milk, if they could send someone to collect it, he would supply it to them. He knew Mr Wigram would be able to send a message to their Majesties with the offer. Arthur had a reply thanking him kindly for thinking of them, but they were fine for now. He felt pleased they responded to his offer of help towards them. Arthur was walking down the street when he saw a man selling tins of pears, peaches, and fruit cocktail. The man wanted ration coupons for them, but Arthur offered him cash, which he accepted. Once Arthur and Rose returned home, she invited Elizabeth and May to tea. Elizabeth had not had tinned fruit for such a long time, but she enjoyed every mouthful with her eyes closed. At the end of the evening, Rose offered her mum and May a tin to take home, but Elizabeth refused telling Rose that she had more mouths to feed than her and May but would come to tea again another day.

Every day was a new day with a new idea, the radio would encourage people to try and help themselves and others for their country. Rose had some old flour sacks in the shed. She took them outside, cutting them open along the seam, taking the string off the side, and then laying them flat. She dyed them with the skins of the beetroots and onions to try and make them darker. Hoping they would turn black, she wanted to use them instead of the shutters on the windows, this would make it easier in the mornings. Rose and Arthur took down the shutters and hung the sacks with two nails and a piece of string. This became their new curtains and was easier to open and close and helped keep their light to a minimum during the night if any enemy planes flew over, as having a light in the countryside would be seen like a beacon. The war was becoming more aggressive. The tabloids were printing updates of the war, the numbers of the deaths and casualties was frightening to Rose.

# Chapter 47

# THE NEVER-ENDING WAR

It was 1943 and Rose was pregnant with another baby, she and Arthur could not believe it. Arthur joked saying that if they have another boy, they will be close to having their own football team. Rose was now 39 years old and though she thought her childbearing days were behind her, they were enthusiastic about having a new member join the family. Rose was tired; she was looking forward to giving birth as it would be easier to move around. She had everything at home she needed for the new arrival, she had knitted hats and matching cardigans. Rose liked new babies clothes to start with, and then use what she already had for the boys. The nappies were now ten years old, the original ones she had from Roy. Most of them were as white as when she had them, but some were a little stained. They had lost their quality as they were all nearly threadbare, but for this last time, Rose was not going to buy anything else for the new baby.

As the days passed Rose hoping for the war to end, so that the new baby would be born in peace time. The trips to town were becoming more crowded. American soldiers had been arriving in the UK to help with the allies resistance against Germany and combat training had been initiated in countryside regions. There was more laughter and singing on the streets of Hereford. To Rose this made her feel happy, as if things were back to normality. She had heard stories of how Americans GI's were going out with the local girls.

The girls were vigorous and playful, which would relax the GI's on their time off, but it was also evident that the attention was enjoyed by the females, as most of the local men were fighting in Europe.

Arthur had not managed to increase the three cows or several sheep in the fields. He was intending to grow his farm, and he wondered if any more payments were coming in for Roy. They had not received any money in the four years since the war had started. To their surprise, a rep from London turned up at the farm. He was one that had visited a few years previously. He had arranged a cot for Roy Albert in his early years and the bed sheets for Jim, Rose remembered this and thanked him. He was happy to see them and spoke of the destruction to the London streets. He told of how his house was blown up and he had lost members of his family. Rose offered him a cup of tea and this time he accepted. He was glad to sit down and rest as he had no driver with him as resources were limited. He called to visit them that day as he had other Palace related business in the area but did not give any further details. As he was leaving, he handed over the envelope to Rose which was much larger than normal. Rose placed the envelope on the mantlepiece, Arthur thanked the rep for coming down from London and they both wished him well on his journey. "I wonder how much money is in it, it's much bigger than normal," Arthur remarked, "Well, you will know, when we open it later. Now get the children and we will all have lunch," Rose replied. Arthur went to get the boys ready for lunch. Rose held Fred and fed him with a bottle of milk, Arthur and Jim passed food across the table to the others, they were all now capable of feeding themselves. Arthur was picking at his food, pausing after every few bites deep in thought, "How much money was in the envelope and what he could buy?" He had many ideas running through his head, so decided to stand up to get the envelope from the mantlepiece. Arthur's eyes glowed with excitement as he looked into the envelope, but Rose teased him by taking it off him and said, "I will put Fred down for a nap," and took the envelope upstairs with her to hide it. Rose returned to the table with Arthur looking disheartened. "Eat your lunch Arthur, and we will open it later." All afternoon as Arthur was working outside, he had many ideas of how he could improve the farm with the extra money from the palace.

When the evening came, Rose washed the children, put their pyjamas on them and they all got into bed. She went back downstairs; Arthur was stoking the fire so that the kettle could be brought to the boil. Rose made a cup of tea for the two of them and then quietly went upstairs to fetch the envelope. On return Arthur was standing by his chair, stirring his tea anxiously to see how much money was inside the envelope. Rose opened it and pulled out the largest amount of white five- and ten-pound notes, they had ever seen at one time. They looked at it in amazement. Rose slowly passed each note to Arthur, he laid it out on the table, and they counted it together. Rose could see Arthur's expression, as he was already planning what to spend it on. "I want to buy a tractor and a new car, what do you think Rose?" She was surprised he was not saving the money for the larger farm he wanted. Rose said "you wanted a larger farm, and this money would give us the chance to buy one. You cannot have both it is a farm, or tractor." He sat back in his chair, contemplating what to buy and what would be most beneficial and available, during the war.

Arthur's car was incredibly old and sometimes would not start, this had been given to him by Elizabeth. Rose would be standing there with the children all dressed ready to go out in the car and watched Arthur cranking the handle repeatedly. He would then begin cursing, which made Rose look at the children and cover her ears for them to follow her action. He would then go into the house with the car plugs on a shovel and warmed them over the fire. Once they were warm, he would take them back and place them in the car, cranking the turning handle again, praying it would start and cheer when he would hear the motor jump and rumble. The children would sit in the back. Roy would have John on his lap, Jim would sit beside them, and Eric would hold Fred who would want to sit in the front with Rose. They enjoyed having the car as it was a lot quicker than the horse and cart, when it worked.

Any car journey would be exciting for the children but frightening for Rose because of the war. Rose and Arthur would tell the children to look out of the window, into the sky, for planes as they worried that the car would not offer protection from any bombing raids. The children would be playing with the mandatory gas masks everyone was issued with by the government. These masks came in a cardboard box which they would have with them at all times, they could be fined if they were seen without their gas masks. Rose and Arthur showed the children numerous times how to put on their gas masks. The school also had routine training with the children at putting on their masks. The boys like to put them on in front of their parents and exhale as this would push the air out and make a rude noise. Rose had a special hooded gas mask for the upcoming birth of the baby, this covered the body of the baby and straps tucked underneath the bottom to fasten like a nappy, leaving the legs out. It had a visor for the baby to see out and for the parent to see in. There was a special pump on the side of the hood allowing air to be pushed into the mask. The metal skullcap gave protection to the occupant if accidentally dropped. Luckily, there was never a time during the war that the family had to put the gasmasks to their real use.

A baby gas mask used in World War 2

# Chapter 48

# IT'S NOT WHAT SHE WANTED

Rose did not want to give birth to another baby during the war, but she didn't have a choice. She knew the baby was coming and asked Jim to fetch the nurse. After carefully examining Rose, the nurse informed her that the baby would probably not be born for some days; and to lay down and rest, she would return the following day to check on how things were progressing. Rose was worried as the nurse was not married and had no children of her own, this caused some doubt over her expertise in this situation. As soon as Rose was on her own with Arthur, she told him that the baby would be coming that day. It was her sixth child after all. Arthur was not sure who to believe, but said to Rose, "rest for now, and we will wait until the nurse returns tomorrow." Arthur went downstairs, Rose lay there thinking about what was going to happen next.

Next thing Rose sat up and was about to get up from the bed, when she felt some discomfort, she knew she was about to give birth. She shouted down to Arthur and the boy's, "the baby is coming, the baby is coming, tell Roy to run and get Mrs Brooks. Tell her the baby is coming." Roy ran to fetch Mrs Brooks from her farm, as fast as he could, yelling out her name as he got closer to the farm, so she would meet him before he got there. "Quickly, mum needs you. She is having the baby." Mrs Brooks was still in her slippers and ran with Roy back to Middle Mill. She went upstairs to find Rose in her bed and took one look and knew the baby was actually coming. There was not much work or effort needed before the baby was introduced to the world. There were no complications, and thankfully Rose had no fever. Mrs Brooks washed off the baby and placed her in Rose's arms. "It's a girl," Mrs Brooks said. Rose let out a loud scream to Mrs Brooks surprise. Arthur and the children heard the scream from downstairs, they ran up to see what was happening. "What's happened? Are you alright?" Arthur was unnerved. Mrs Brooks told him that everything was fine, and that Rose was well. Mrs Brooks let Arthur stay in the room to be by his wife, and asked the boy's to go back downstairs, as she would be down in a moment. He could see Rose covered in the bed covers, tears streaming down her face, with the baby wrapped in a blanket next to her. Arthur looked at the baby who had its eyes closed. He thought that it was dead. His eyes began to tear up, when Mrs Brooks picked up the baby, and the baby opened her eyes. Arthur looked surprised and turned to Rose, "What's wrong?" Rose started sobbing, "It's a girl." They could both see that Rose was disappointed with having a girl. Mrs Brooks told Rose to rest in bed for a while, and she would wash and wrap the baby, before putting her into her cot. Mrs Brooks and Arthur returned downstairs to the boys who were waiting to hear that they were both alright. "What are we going to call this one dad?" John asked. Arthur sat in his chair, "I have no idea, it's a girl." This excited the boys, to have a sister was something new to them. Arthur was just as upset as Rose having a girl, but he was trying not to show it. Mrs Brooks couldn't understand why they were disappointed, as they had a perfectly healthy baby. Rose and Arthur's lack of excitement bothered her, but she just put it down to the fact that it was Rose's sixth child.

Once Mrs Brooks left the Mill, Roy went upstairs to see his mother and his new baby sister. "What's her name mum?" Rose said to Roy that she had not thought of any girl's names, and they could all have a think about what names they liked. Arthur thought it would be best to call her after Rose, and then pick something pretty for her second name. Rose got up out of bed, and carefully moved around the room as she still felt fatigued. She went over to the cot and looked at her sleeping baby, Rose knew that she would need more care than the boys. Roy was leaning on the side of the cot looking at his sleeping sister. "She's the most beautiful baby I have ever seen." Rose placed her hand on Roy's head stroking his hair. She could see the baby looked like an angel but in her heart, she didn't want her and sadly, openly said so. That evening as Arthur and Rose were talking, they decided to name their new baby girl Rose after her mother, and Violet after the beautiful, perfumed flowers. Arthur would say it's a pretty name for a pretty girl. Rose hated it when he said things like that, as it was soppy and sentimental.

As the weeks passed and Rose was ready to go to Hereford market with her new baby. Other mothers with their own children would stop and talk to Rose, they would remark on the beauty of her new baby, but this would not change the feelings Rose felt about Rose Violet. Her boys were strong, and she knew they would be able to get on in life. They would work hard and make their own way and marry, and not be reliant on others. Rose could only imagine her daughter going through what she did, suffering heartbreak of the worst kind, she did not want that. She had taught the boys to be strong, as feelings or emotions would make them weak. How could she teach her daughter to be like one of the boys? Rose had decided that this baby was definitely the last. She knew Arthur was not too bothered about that part of their relationship, and so she told him that was that. They were not to have sex again as she did not want to risk having another daughter. Arthur was fine with that, as he told her that it was not something he would ever miss with her. They were both now in their forties and he often wondered how they had so many children. He could count how many times they slept together on one hand, and he thought it was strange, he never once questioned it.

Rose dissatisfied with her life and the never-ending war. She often felt guilty about her life. A husband who was with her, farming, rather than fighting the war. Five sons that were still too young to join the fight.

The sadness she heard from neighbours and soldiers about those that had died on the battlefields and the increasing number of wounded soldiers returning, disfigured. Priests would come out to the country from the town and hold special services on a regular basis. They would pray for the soldiers that were overseas and for the dead and wounded. It became a normal routine for most people in the country to experience that.

After one of the special services Rose went to visit Mrs Brooks. Violet was now six months old, and Rose had been to see Mrs Brooks quite often, but this time it wasn't with happiness or joy, it was with sadness and regret. She told Mrs Brooks she was finding it very difficult in bonding with Violet. Violet was growing into the most beautiful little girl with curly dark hair and big brown eyes. Everyone loved her apart from her mother. Rose could not help but think, that life would bring her daughter heartbreak. Rose was raised with the idea that a girl is to run the house and be a mother. Boys on the other hand, would have a different life full of adventure, and so Rose asked Mrs Brooks if she would help find a surrogate family for Violet.

At Mill farm Rose was hard on Violet, showing no love towards her, treating her the same as the boys when they were younger. Arthur on the other hand would be kind and gentle towards her. Rose would often go into the bedroom to find Roy playing games with Violet on the floor. This did not please Rose as she had been put in her cot to sleep. At one point, she came in to find Arthur leaning over the cot and chatting away to his daughter. Although he did not pick her up as he chatted to her, he felt she needed some attention. Rose told Arthur that she had asked Mrs Brooks to help find a new family for Violet. Arthur said, "that's a good idea, as a girl would not be as helpful on the farm." The boys hated the idea that their mum and dad were giving their sister away. They would tickle her when they played with her, she would giggle, and this made the boy's smile.

Jim was now living at the Weir Farm in Ewyas Harold, this farm was left to Rose by her aunt. He set off to visit his brothers at the Mill, and on arrival Roy told him that their sister was to be given away. Jim was not impressed with what he heard from Roy. He told Roy that when the time was right, he would speak to their mother alone. It was no good speaking to her in front of Arthur because what he had to say to his mother, would definitely cause trouble between them. Jim stayed for a while and discussed with his mum and Arthur what work needed doing at the Weir Farm. Arthur told him he was available to stay and help at the farm for a few days. Jim said, "some help would be most appreciated." Rose offered Roy to join them, knowing there would be tension between them if they were left alone. That would leave Rose with the rest of the children at home.

At the Weir Farm, Jim, Roy, and Arthur, repaired some of the fencing around the fields. Jim said, "that should keep those sheep from walking through the hedge, and off the hay meadows." Roy and Arthur agreed, it was a fine job done. This took them a whole three days. They didn't have very good meals while they were there, as nobody had been into the village to buy food. Jim could boil eggs on the fire but had no spare bread to make toast. They only had enough bread and cheese as their main meal. Both, Arthur, and Roy were constantly feeling hungry and tired after the day's work. Jim was glad of the help from Arthur and Roy, but having his own farm made him feel more independent. When they got back to Middle Mill, Rose had cooked a full meal of potatoes, meat, and vegetables. Arthur understood now why Jim was always hungry when he came to visit. He mentioned to Rose that Jim was not eating properly. Rose said she would speak to Jim and tell him that he could come over and eat with them, anytime he wanted. Rose knew Arthur was a little more placid towards Jim, but Jim only visited occasionally as he still remembered how Arthur would hit him as a boy.

The following week, Arthur offered help to May at the Lawns. He and Roy would come over and cut the grass meadow down for hay, as the weather was looking good for the rest of the week. Elizabeth was nearly eighty years old and was finding it difficult to move around the house. May was struggling to look after the farm and her mother. They knew Rose had her hands full with all the children and the Mill Farm, so they did not like to ask her for help. May would say to everyone that Rose had the children and so she should look after them as their mother. She was disgusted at the thought of Rose giving away one of her children, no matter if it was a boy or a girl. May loved Violet and couldn't think about someone else having her. It broke her heart, as Violet was family too.

Mrs Brooks had found a wonderful couple to take Violet. They had a large house in Hereford and had their own staff. The husband was a banker, and his wife could not have children herself. She brought them to meet Rose and Arthur and Violet. Arthur was happy for them to take his daughter straight away, but Rose wanted to see the house where Violet would live, before she gave her daughter away. Once Roy knew that these people had come to the house to take away his sister, he knew he had to get a message to Jim. Jim said he could stop mum giving her away. It took all the money he had to get the bus that went halfway towards Ewyas Harold. He was nervous about this as he was on his own and had not been on a bus before. Moreover, he was worried that he hadn't told his mum and dad where he was going. He got off the bus as it stopped in Pontrilas, he then ran in the direction of Ewyas Harold. He didn't get far before stopping to catch his breath, and as he continued walking, a car pulled up beside him, and the young lady driving offered him a lift. She asked where he was going, and he told her he was going to Ewyas Harold to see his brother. She said, "I'm going that way, jump in and I will drop you off there." The car pulled away fast, Roy held on tight as this car was much quicker than the one his dad had. Roy asked, "what sort of car is it." She was not too sure, as it was her father's, and she just took it to go for a drive. Although Roy appreciated the lift, he was not sure if she did have permission to drive the car, and when he got to Jim's, he told her to take it back before she got into trouble. She did not say anything as she waved him goodbye before speeding off. Jim was out in the shed fixing another car engine, something he liked to do. If he could get them working, he would sell them but if he could not, he would use them as spare parts, as people were always asking him to fix their cars. Roy told him how he had caught the bus and then got a lift with a stranger to get to him. Jim was not impressed and warned him not to tell their mother or he would get into a lot of trouble. "Why are you here anyway?" He asked. Roy began tearing up, "They have found a family for Violet. They want them to take her away and you said you could stop it." Jim put down his tools, he cleaned his hands and told Roy to get into the car. They both drove back towards Middle Mill to confront their parents.

# Chapter 49

# LOOKING OUT FOR HIS SISTER

When they arrived back at Mill farm, the car that had brought the banker to the house had gone. Roy and Jim went into the house and straight upstairs. Jim looked in the cot and there was Violet, fast asleep. He gently rubbed her head and then saw his mother looking in the door. "I want a word with you, if that's alright?" Jim said looking at his mum. Rose looked at Jim with curiosity, "Is everything alright?" Jim began walking out of the bedroom and downstairs with Rose following. "Where's Arthur?" He asked. Rose began worrying as to why Jim was there. "He's gone to see May, but he will be back soon if you want a word with him. What's wrong?" Jim was relieved that Arthur wasn't there as he could speak with his mother. As they both headed outside, Jim told his younger brothers to stay inside and look after their sister.

Rose and Jim walked to the other side of the Mill house. No one ever knew what he said to his mother that day, but Violet was going nowhere. Rose told the banker and his wife, that they had changed their mind, and that they could not part with Violet. Rose told Arthur she had decided to keep Violet, and no more was ever said about how she wanted to get rid of her daughter.

There were talks of the war coming to an end. The people were excited for that day but were remaining cautious as it was something they had heard for many years. Newspapers were reporting that Hitler and the Nazis were near defeat.

The British, Americans and the Red Army were surrounding Germany and moving towards Berlin. People of Hereford were buzzing, talking of how things will change in the near future. Rose was just as excited to hear the war was coming to an end. She was thrilled to receive a letter from Jean Hughes. She had not heard from her in such a long time. Rose opened the letter with a big smile but as she began reading it, her smile dropped, and she held her hand over her mouth with sadness. Jean had written to Rose telling her of the death of her beloved Samual. He had been killed fighting in the war and his body was not brought home. Rose was upset as she knew how much Jean loved her husband. It was still something Rose never felt for Arthur, but she compared it to the love she felt for David. By the end of the letter, Rose was sobbing, and felt miserable all afternoon. Arthur did not say anything to Rose, as he could see she was upset. She had only met Samual once or twice in passing in London before Jean got together with him. Violet started crying so Rose picked her up off the floor and rocked her. As she gazed down at her, she could see this wide-eyed child smiling at her, for the first time, she noticed the beauty of her daughter. Rose stood up out of the chair, and grabbing a bonnet off the side, she carried Violet out into the sunshine. She put the bonnet on her to keep the sun off her head, and sat down on the grass, putting Violet down next to her. The boys, Eric, John, and Fred came out of the house and sat next to them on the grass. Mum said, "if you all pick me some daisies, I will show you how to make them into a chain." They all began picking daisies, for their mum. She showed them how to split the stem with their nails and place one daisy through the other to form a chain. Eric and John picked this up quite quick, they were quite good at it. Fred on the other hand was still a bit young to grasp the technique. Rose split a pile for him so he could have a go making his own daisy chain, the same as his brothers. Arthur came across the field and found them all sitting on the grass, playing with the flowers. It was like he was watching an entirely different family. As much as Rose never let any harm come to the children, he had never seen her so playful and caring.

Arthur could now see that he had a family growing and that this would help him run the farm he always wanted. With his age and experience, he realised that money was not everything and his dream in life was to get his farm. He knew it would be soon because of the money they had saved over the past 12 years. The money sent from the palace to look after Roy, as he was of Royal blood line. A member of the royal family had bought nearly everything they owned, and he was grateful for it. He felt he had looked after Jim and Roy as his own and did not think they would have been treated better by anyone else. He thought that when he had his farm, the boys could work it and he would be in charge. He would spend many hours thinking of having the best herd of milking cows, the biggest flock of sheep, his life would be perfect. He was ready to wait until everything fell into place.

# Chapter 50

# WAR IS OVER

On the 2nd of May 1945, News arrived around the world from Germany, Hitler is dead. Killed at his command post in Berlin, this made the end of the war more realistic for many people. Six days later, on the 8th of May 1945, Winston Churchill announced VE day, Victory in Europe. The country joined together to celebrate and remember the sacrifices so many people made over those dark years. There were street parties everywhere and while they were in town, the family were invited to several. Rose wanted the children to celebrate that the war was over, and they sat down on a long table in the middle of the street, eating jam sandwiches and cake. They wore hats in the shape of crowns and sang songs with their arms around one another. This was with friends, neighbours, and strangers, who all came together for this historic and joyful moment. They all went home from the party feeling tired, after so much food and excitement.

Rose and Arthur both felt that now would be the time for them to move on with their plans, to purchase a larger farm; but this would not be the case for quite some time. Yes, the war had ended but not that much had changed. The shops were short of stock; rations were still in place, and Soldiers were yet to return from overseas. Parts of the country was suffering from the bombing of homes and businesses. Unexploded bombs were littered around the City's and the countryside, dropped by German aircraft. Farms were not easily available to buy at this time, Rose and Arthur looked at many local regions, as they were keen to move on and start a fresh.

In 1946, Arthur would visit the cattle market each time there was a sale. He wanted to buy more cows, at one sale he managed to buy two, Arthur was so pleased with them, they were delivered to the Mill a few days later. When Rose came out of the house to look at the new cows, she could not believe what stood before her eyes. Arthur had clearly rushed into buying them, they both looked lean, and one of them was walking lame. He said, "they will soon fill out, once they have some grub." He managed to put a halter on the cow that was lame, as he needed to look at her leg. Arthur tied the halter around his hand and bent down to lift the cows leg, and as he did, the cow who was having none of this, took off so fast and knocked Arthur to the ground. She was dragging Arthur along the grass, kicking, and tossing her head, thankfully the halter slipped off, and Arthur lay on the ground wondering what had just happened. Rose and the children had stood well back, and they roared with laughter at the sight of the mad cow and Arthur going across the field. Roy shouted out she does not look so lame now. Arthur stood up brushing himself down, cursing and swearing as he headed back towards the house. Rose took the children indoors and put the kettle on ready for tea, knowing that when Arthur came in, he would be angry at what had just happened. After tea Arthur went out to milk the cows.

Arthur managed to get the lame cow to follow their house cow into the shed, the other new cow was said to be in calf, and dry (not giving milk) although she followed along behind. The food was in front of the milking Bale (where the cows were milked). The new cow was stressed from all that had happened that day and held her milk, as she nervously looked around at what Arthur was doing. Once she had started eating the nuts from the bucket, she began to calm, and her milk started to flow. Arthur decided not to sit on his milking stool, just in case the cow kicked out, he bent over leaning against her. He had managed to fill half a bucket of milk, just as the cow had run out of food, and she became jittery. She pulled back in the bale and stood on Arthur's foot, he quickly stood up with a shout, knocking over the bucket of milk. Rose heard all the commotion coming across the yard, went outside to see what was happening, "do you need any help" she asked Arthur. "Yes, open the bloody door so I can let this cow out!" Rose opened the door, the cow barged past her knocking her over, this upset the other cow causing her to run out, just missing Rose. Arthur limped towards Rose asking, "are you alright? I didn't want them both to get out, the one has not been milked properly." Rose glared at him, "you should never have bought it in the first place, but as usual Arthur knows best." Rose walked back to the house, a few minutes later Arthur came in, "I hope she will settle in the morning, she just needs time, and then we will think about what we can do with her." Rose just looked at him but did not say a word.

The following morning Arthur was up early, the sun was shining through the window, and he wanted to have a good look over his cows. He went to the cow shed and prepared the Bale for milking, with three buckets of food. Arthur approached the cows that were waiting at the gate, he then opened the gate only wide enough to let the two cows through that he wanted. As they walked to the shed, Arthur moved slowly along behind, he did not want to trouble the new cow. In the shed he put the chain around the cows neck, after milking his house cow first, Arthur then moved his stool, putting the bucket of milk to one side, as he did not want to knock it over. He put the bucket of food in front of her, talking to her all the time as he milked her; as soon as she finished her food, she began to move side to side, Arthur moved the bucket of milk and placed the fresh bucket of food in front of her, and finished milking her. As she was stood there Arthur looked at her foot and noticed a nail in the bottom of it. After fetching some pliers from the shed, he pulled out the nail. There was some bleeding but not too much for Arthur to be concerned. He was pleased with how she milked that morning, and he went into the house telling Rose.

Rose was in the kitchen giving the children breakfast, Arthur was excited to tell her, that he had found why the new cow was lame. He also said to Rose, "the grass at the lawns that we cut the other day needs turning over to dry," and he was going to the lawns to turn the hay and would not be back until late. Rose said she was still vext from the night before and did not care what time he came home. After Arthur, Roy, and Eric, had left to go to the lawns Rose continued with her day, cleaning the house, sewing, and looking after the children. The evening was approaching, and Rose assumed she would have to milk the cows, as she had no idea what time Arthur and the boys would be back. Rose asked John to watch Fred and Violet while she went out to get the cows in. She went into the cow shed and filled the three buckets with food, remembering everything Arthur had said that morning. Rose then went to the field the two cows were at the gate waiting to come in for their food. She opened the gate, they walked through and straight towards the cow shed. Rose followed Arthur's instructions from the morning milking. When she had finished the house cow, she moved the bucket of milk to the side, she then placed one of the buckets of food in front of the new cow. Everything was going well until the cow was nearing the end of her food, she became fidgety, moving from side to side and swishing her tail. Whipping from side to side, her tail hit Rose in the side of the head. Rose placed the second bucket of food in front of her, and resumed milking, then a swish of the tail caught Rose across her face. The tail hair hitting Rose in the eye, she had never felt such pain, she put her hand over her eye as it started to water. The pain was excruciating, she staggered backwards knocking over the bucket of milk, she could not keep either eye open, panicking as there was no one to help her. Rose felt her way to the door, trying as hard as she could to open her eye, she felt sick with the pain. On reaching the door she opened it and thought she was heading towards the house, not realising she was heading towards the field. Rose called out hoping John or Fred would answer her, she heard voices she called louder, it was Arthur and the boys. They helped Rose into the house, Arthur put a cold wet flannel on her face, Rose was in agony and asked him to take her to the hospital. Arthur was tired and could not understand why his tea was not ready; he became angrier when he was told his cows were still chained in the shed. Rose pleaded to go to the hospital, but he was having none of it. Roy and Eric were terribly upset, they could do nothing to help their mum, Roy put the children to bed, and Arthur put the cows back in the field. That night Rose slept in the chair, holding a wet compress over her eye, and Arthur went up to bed. In the morning when he got up, he realised Rose needed to go to the hospital. Arthur drove to the Lawns and fetched May to sit with the children, he then took Rose to the Hereford Eye Hospital. There the Doctor informed her if she had gone to the hospital in the evening, they may have saved her sight in the eye; but has she had left it too long there was nothing they could do for her. The Doctor asked Arthur why she was not brought in as soon as it had happened, he told the Doctor she would not come, no matter what he said to persuade her. Rose was devastated with the loss of sight in her one eye, it took her many months to get used to the vision she now had.

# Chapter 51

# 1947

The year was 1947, the children were growing up. Roy was fourteen, Eric was twelve, John was nine, Fred was seven and Violet was four and a half, going on five. Arthur was over the far field loading up the trailer with bales of hay, so they could be moved into the barn. Rose was looking out of the window, and thought the stack was too high on the trailer, so she went to tell him, but he took no notice. She called the children, so she knew where they were, not to get in the way of the tractor and trailer. Rose had a feeling that it was not safe for Arthur to go down a steep bank with such a high load. She watched as the tractor slowly went down across the field, the trailer following behind. Suddenly, the tractor started to pick up speed and Arthur could not slow it down. He steered the tractor back towards the incline of the bank, hoping this would help stop it. As the tractor turned, the trailer jack-knifed tipping it over. Rose could see what was happening but could not do anything about it. She asked Fred to make sure Violet stayed with him and to take her indoors. Rose started to run across to where the tractor had come to a stop. She could hear a high-pitched noise and realised it was herself screaming in panic. She got halfway down the bank when someone passed her, was it Roy? When they reached the tractor, which was laying on its side, she could see Arthur in the brook. She then realized that it was one of the farmhands from the next farm over, who had passed by her. He had heard the commotion, and sent his colleague to get Mr Brooks, they saw Arthur and the tractor running away down the field from where they were working. The three of them were there in what seemed a matter of minutes. They pulled Arthur out of the water. He was in shock and not making any sense, in and out of consciousness. Mr Brooks got the tractor with the flat trailer attached to it. They carried Arthur up the bank and put him onto the trailer, wrapped him in a blanket, Mr Brooks then set off to Hereford hospital with Arthur. He was in hospital for several days, and when Rose went to visit, she couldn't believe what she saw. Arthur was in plaster from the neck down, he was a solid block, as he had spinal damage.

The day Arthur was discharged from hospital, Frank took him home. Rose ran around the house doing everything for him. He was miserable and moaned a lot, but as usual, Rose put up with his moaning and got on with what she had to do. Rose decided to apply for a driving license, as she thought that if she could drive, they would never be stuck again. Arthur did not want her to drive, it would give her independence from him, and he would no longer be needed. One thing about Rose, she was a strong-minded person and if she decided to do something Arthur could not stop her.

Every quarter, the money came in for Roy. He was doing well at school and was very good at maths. It was a subject he enjoyed, he would have liked to have gone on to be an accountant, but instead farming would take priority. Roy said to his mother what he wanted to do, "could you speak to the school mum," he asked. Rose was finding every day hard and was not in the mood to upset Roy about school. She went to the school with Roy to speak to his teacher, with the worry of the farm on her mind. She spoke to the teacher and explained it mattered not what Roy wanted. He had to leave school at the end of term as he was fourteen and was needed to work on the farm. The teacher tried reasoning with Rose. He said, "Roy needs to go onto further education, he's top of his class, and I can't do any more for him." Rose would have none of it, she did not care about Roy's education. He was to be a farmer and that was that. Roy was sad that his mother did not care about what he wanted to do with his life. Rose was in charge and that was that. Eric, on the other hand, who sadly was far from bright, did not want to go to school, he wanted to work on the farm, but had to wait until he was fourteen to leave.

Rose was getting more and more frustrated with Arthur as she was finding it difficult, having to do everything for him. She would shave him, sometimes nicking his skin with the razor. He would then blame her for not shaving him properly; he would mutter at Rose, she would tell him that he could stop whining, or shave himself. As Rose washed him, he would contend that he is not a baby, Rose knew a baby would not be so much trouble. But when it came to wiping his backside, both of them hated it, but it had to be done. Arthur would sometimes be that upset that he would say to Rose that he wished he were dead. Instead of Rose supporting him, she would agree with him. He lay in bed for weeks grumbling and groaning about how Rose could not do things right instead of being grateful to her.

The following morning while Rose was washing Arthur, he noticed he had feeling in his lower legs. Rose asked him to try and move his toes, and when they moved slightly, they both smiled together. The Doctor at the hospital, said that he may not be able to walk again, but this was a good sign that Arthur was on the mend. He was an impatient chap and he had had enough of being in bed and wanted to have his old life back. After a few more weeks Frank took Arthur back to hospital to have his plaster cast removed. He had some strength back into his legs with the help of Rose. The Doctors carefully cut away the plaster cast and explained to Arthur that his back would feel weak, he should only carry out light exercise, taking plenty of rest. "It will take many months to build the strength up in your body," the doctor told him.

Back at home, Arthur was sat in his chair by the fire. He found it uncomfortable sitting up right, in the same position for more than a short time. Violet wanted to sit on his lap, she wondered where the plaster had gone? She would sit next to her dad in bed and play a tune on his plaster cast, with the spoons. This kept Violet amused for a while as Arthur lay there, unable to move. After a short time, this would annoy him and he would call Rose, who would pretend not to hear him. Now Arthur was feeling stiff, he did not want Violet to sit on his lap. He did not want any of the children around him at all. He wanted to be left alone.

# Chapter 52

# REMEMBER WHO YOU ARE

Rose could see Roy was upset at having to finish school but there was no more she could do. He was needed to work on the farms, the Lawns and Middle Mill. Arthur had an understanding why Roy wanted an education so he could become a gentleman. As Arthur worshiped Mr Wigram and he would have loved to have had a son of the same standing. Rose also wanted the best for Roy, but that would have meant he would be different to his siblings, at that point, with all her other troubles, she could not manage to let Roy go off in a different direction.

Roy finished his last term at school and began working on the farm full-time. Arthur began taking his first steps outside, since his accident. He found it difficult but was determined, not to let his recovery get in the way. He walked around the farm with two walking sticks. Everyone could see how hard it was for him to walk about, but he brushed this aside and wanted to get on with the work. Arthur decided he would go across the field to see his cows. Standing near the gate, he went to open it, and then, he could not move. His legs would not move, it was as if he was frozen to the ground. He could not lift his feet, this caused him to panic and yell out for help. Rose and the boys were doing their chores around the house and did not hear his cries for help. He waited and waited but no one came, and he began to get tired holding on to the gate. Next thing he was on the ground. The grass was dry as the sun was hot that day, all Arthur could do was lay there, hoping they would come looking for him. Rose had been enjoying the peace and quiet, and realised she had not heard Arthur moaning, she began wondering what he was up to. She sent the children out to see if they could find him. They walked around the sheds but there was no sign of him. Eric, John, and Fred went across the field to see the cows, they found Arthur on the ground by the gate. There was no response from him, as they tried to wake him. Fred ran back to the house, fighting back the tears, crying for his mum to come and help, as their dad was dead. Rose ran after Fred, back to where Arthur was found, the other children sobbing with Eric kneeling beside him. Rose moved Eric to one side and knelt down next to Arthur, calling out his name and pulling on his jumper. "Come on Arthur don't do this. Come on, wake up." She could see at that point that he was not dead, but not very responsive. She pulled at his arm, and he opened his eyes. "I can't move my legs." At first, Rose did not know what to do. She touched him on one of his legs and asked if he could feel her hand. He nodded and said yes. Rose touched the other leg and he felt that too. They helped him to sit up against the gate, Rose asked him to bend his legs, they would all help him up. Arthur tried and tried but had no strength to lift his legs. Rose continued asking Arthur to bend his legs, but he kept crying out that he could not. She let go of his arm, and before he fell back down, the children pushed his back against the gate. Rose stormed off to the shed and came back with the wheelbarrow. She pointed to it and told Arthur "if you can't get up, you will have to go in it." He was not impressed, "I'll stay here for now!" He said, as he wasn't going in any wheelbarrow. He asked them to go and get help from the neighbours. Rose was adamant that she was going to get him back to the house herself. They dragged Arthur around and the boys held him, while Rose tilted the wheelbarrow so the front of it was pressing against his back, and the children helped pull him into it. Looking like a scarecrow waiting to be erected, with his legs hanging over the edge of the wheelbarrow, Rose pushed him to the backdoor. At that point, she had no idea how to get him out. Eric and Fred stood by the wheelbarrow, chuckling to themselves, if only their dad could see himself now. Rose could hear Roy coming out of the cowshed, she shouted to him for help. As soon as he got to them, he burst out laughing at the sight of Arthur laying there like a rag doll. Roy helped his mother tilt the wheelbarrow up so Arthur's feet were on the ground, and then he and Rose held Arthur by the arms, as Eric and John pulled the wheelbarrow back. Arthur was once again standing but needed help moving into the house. They got him to his chair so he could make himself comfortable. He was exhausted, like they all were, but Rose made him a cup of tea all the while berating him for going outside in the first place. As if she did not already have enough to do. After she had recovered from this ordeal, and the children had had their tea, she asked Arthur how he was feeling. She wanted him to go to the hospital, but Arthur did not, it frightened him, he wasn't going back in plaster. It took several days before Arthur ventured outside again. He told everyone when he wanted to go outside and made sure one of the children were with him just in case, he had another fall.

It was not long before he was back on the tractor, lifting anything caused him great pain in his back. Roy and Eric did all the lifting and carrying for him around the farm. As time passed, Arthur's health had improved and all he wanted was the farm of his dreams, with a large house and hundreds of acres. He wanted to find this farm as soon as possible, with Roy growing into a young man, he had no idea how long the money would keep coming in. He was amazed that they were still paying for Roy after all this time, as they had lost King George V, and David (Edward VIII) the Prince of Wales, had abdicated in less than a year. Arthur thought to himself, if Queen Mary passes away, the money is bound to stop, and she was in her late 70s just after the war had ended. He spoke to Rose, "We need to get a new farm as soon as we can, in case the money stops coming in." Rose agreed so Arthur went out in search for a new farm. There was nothing for sale that suited him, but he kept looking with the hope of finding his dream farm.

**Roy Albert Powell (third row centre) School Photograph**

# Chapter 53

# MOULDING A LIFE FOR YOURSELF

In 1947, Roy finished Lord Scudamore School at the age of 14. He was top of his maths class, the teacher told Rose there was nothing else he could teach him at the school, and that she should consider further education for him. Rose was unable to let Roy go to university at that time, but she was insistent on him going to an agriculture college. Roy waited until 1951 and then he went to Shropshire Farm Institute, Walford, for two years, studying a course in General Agriculture. Eric worked at Mill Farm, while Fred, John, and Violet, were still in school. Their lives carried on, nothing but the mundane tasks of running the farm. No major events impacted the family over the years as time passed. Roy finished college in 1953 and went to work at Blackbrook Farm, Skenfirth. This was to give him a different experience of farm work, and for the first time he earned a proper wage. He had joined the young farmers, and at one of their pub meetings, he met his future wife, Rosemary Jones. Arthur finally come across his dream farm and in 1955, he bought The Maerdy Farm in Monmouthshire.

It was a large six-bedroom house, but it had no electricity or a bathroom. Soon after they moved in, Rose insisted on changing the smaller bedroom to a bathroom. She wanted the same as she had seen at the Palace and York House. A bath, a sink unit, and an indoor toilet with a flush. When the engineer came to install the electricity into the house, they had a choice of how many rooms they wanted it in. Rose had it installed in every room, including the cellar. The rooms were also dressed to the highest standard they could afford. Every room was furnished, and the curtains lined and heavy. Arthur had noticed the money from the Palace had stopped arriving, although Rose never seemed short of money to pay for things, if she needed them. He asked Rose if she had heard anything from anyone about the money, but she told him she had not heard anything. They needed to get on to the Milk Marketing Board to get a quoter for their milk, and he needed more cows to increase their herd. Arthur thought of ringing the Palace, but Rose did not want him interfering in anything. Rose had sorted everything with the palace herself and did not want Arthur to know.

It had been several weeks since Jim had taken Rose into Hereford, just the two of them. They had gone to the bank and Rose had opened an account, so the money was to be paid directly to her and no further payments of cash were to be made. Rose liked the idea as she didn't want Arthur to know, she would be in charge of all the finances. Arthur and Eric bought many milking cows from the market. They built up a large herd and had a good quoter from the Milk Marketing Board. Each month, it brought in a cheque which kept Arthur happy. He did very little around the farm himself. He wanted to be a gentleman farmer but would take the time to inspect the boys' work and moan continuously, mostly about nothing important. The house was beautiful, Rose would entertain guests and thoroughly enjoyed it, while Arthur stopped holding conversations with anyone, especially if they asked where the money came from.

In 1955, when Jean Hughes paid them a visit, she wanted to tell the children how and where she met their mother, but Rose didn't want them to know, so she always interrupted

Jean to change the subject. "No one needs to hear about your London days," she moaned to Jean. "But they were our London days Rose. Not just mine." Rose dismissed this and told Jean not to talk about the past. When it was time for Jean to go, she saw Roy standing by the door, she took a moment to pause in amazement, "You look just like your father," she said, as she smiled at him. Roy seemed puzzled about this, but had a brief episode of déjà vu, he recalled moments in his younger years of similar remarks, so he made an excuse to leave and went to see his older brother, Jim.

As he pulled into the Weir Farm, he saw Jim covered in grease and oil. He was bent over a car fixing an engine, Jim stood up and approached Roy, asking, "what do you want." Roy told Jim that their mother's old friend, Jean Hughes, had visited them at the Maerdy that day. "I bet that was interesting. How did the old man feel about it?" Jim quizzed. "He didn't say much to her. In fact, I can't remember him saying anything. He seemed to keep away from the room when Jean was talking. As soon as Jean said anything, mum would shut her up, but she told me, as she was leaving, that I look just like my father. What does she mean by that?" Roy queried. Jim wiped his hands down with a cloth and stared at Roy, "I can tell you the truth if you really want to know it. I know everything and have done for years. Why do you think I got so much out of mother?" Roy was curious to know everything Jim knew, but nervous to hear what was going to be said.

Roy took a breath and nodded to Jim. Your father is a chap from London, mum worked for him. She only worked there for a short while and then you were on the way. Roy didn't know what Jim was implying. "Was I born against her will? Was I forced upon her?" Jim quickly shot down those questions, "No. Nothing like that. Mum really loved your father, in fact, I think he was the only chap she ever loved. I don't think she ever loved my father, but she really did love yours." Roy leant against the wall, "tell me more. Who was he?" Jim looked Roy straight in the eye to keep his attention, and to show he was telling the truth. "Well. This is going to be a shocker. It was the Prince of Wales, Edward VIII, but mum called him David, as of his close friends. When mum did a job on his mother's dress, she met him at his place. They had a relationship and she got pregnant. Who do you think paid for you and the rest of us all these years?" Roy was confused but listening to what was being said, as Jim continued. "Can't you remember the men in the bowler hats that came to visit, we would be sent outside in all kinds of weather, so they wouldn't see us? They were the ones who gave mum the money for keeping you a secret." Roy said, "I remember the slap I had off mum, for asking about the man in the bowler hat." Jim continued giving Roy more information, "In the old man's office, there's a pile of letters he always hid. They are from the King, and they talk about you and the money and the Title." It took Roy a few seconds to take in all the new information. "Title? What Title?" Jim told Roy of how Arthur had insisted on a title for Roy after his death. "You will be called Lord Glasbury, fair does good, old King George, gave it to him to shut him up." Roy said, "I don't know anything about a title. Why have we never heard about it?" Jim leant onto the wing of the car, he knew the conversation was going to go on for a while, explaining everything to Roy. "When he first had the title, he told everyone, but he was not allowed to say why he had it or where he got the money from, so he stopped telling everyone. He was given a medallion with a ribbon on it, which he wore around his neck. It's still there at the house and worth a few bob. When you go back, go into Arthur's office, and read the letters for yourself. But be careful when you ask him about it. He is still a bit touchy on the subject and make sure he is in a good mood, so he doesn't have a go at mum." Roy thanked Jim for finally telling him everything.

On the drive back to the Maerdy Farm, Roy thought about what Jim had told him and wasn't sure how to say or speak to his mum and Arthur. They both had tempers and would keep everything from him if they wanted to. They never thought of telling Roy the truth on the subject as they thought it would be best for Roy not to know. Roy pulled in the drive, and he could see his mother, Rose walking to feed the hens. He waited for her to be out of earshot of the house and went to talk to her.

"Mum, I want to ask you something about my father and I don't mean dad." Rose looked at him but wasn't shocked. "I knew this day would come. I heard Jean when she told you, you look like your father." Roy told her he went to see Jim and was told everything but wanted to hear it from her. "I don't think he told you everything. He only knows parts of it. What did he tell you?" Roy became more nervous and couldn't get the words out. Rose looked him in the eyes. "Yes. David the Prince of Wales, as he was known, is your father. He knows you exist and that's it. Now, help me collect these eggs and don't mention it to Arthur. Well, not today anyway." Roy took a moment to accept all he had been told, he did not know what else to say or do at that moment. He went into the hen house and collected the eggs for his mum. His heart was pounding, and he was trembling. It was not easy for him to accept what he had heard; he knew by the tone in her voice, and the way that his mum looked at him, she was telling him the truth.

Time had passed and Roy became engaged to his fiancée, Rosemary. This upset his mother, as she didn't want her son to marry her. Sadly, some of Rosemary's siblings were suffering from muscular dystrophy, Rose didn't want this to burden Roy, or be passed through to her grandchildren. Roy didn't care what his mother thought as it was his choice. He was still working at Blackbrook Farm and knew he could have a tied cottage when he and Rosemary were married. One evening Roy sat Rosemary down and explained to her, who his real father was, and told her not to tell anybody. She of course, told her family and then the news started to spread like wildfire, and it eventually came back to Rose. She was not impressed with Roy, and asked Arthur what she should do about it. "tell him the truth, let him know who he really is. Now the money has stopped, I don't care who knows." Arthur stated. Rose looked at him with anger, "the money never stopped. I still get it every quarter. It's put into my own bank account." Rose could see the rage in Arthur's face, through gritted teeth he began to growl, "Hiding it from me, were you? You bitch!" With that, he picked up the tea caddy from the kitchen table and hurled it at Rose's head. Luckily, Rose ducked in-time and it missed her, hitting the wall behind, sending tea leaves everywhere. Arthur stormed out, swearing as he left. Rose avoided him for the rest of the afternoon. She could hear him outside, shouting and carrying on at the boys. Over the next few days, the atmosphere was awful in the house. Rose and Arthur never spoke a word to one another, there was silence at the table when they ate. All the boys could see there was a problem but none of them mentioned it.

Roy and Rosemary on their engagement at Monmouth Show 1953

# Chapter 54

# THE APPLE DOESN'T FALL
# FAR FROM THE TREE

Roy went to visit his mother and siblings at the Maerdy Farm. He asked her if it would be possible for him to get in touch with his father Edward. He would like to let him know that he existed and wished to speak with him. Rose had no hesitation in asking Arthur if he would talk to Mr Wigram so that Roy could find out about his father. That day, Arthur wasn't so agreeable, he was settled in his new lifestyle, and he didn't want to venture down that road again. The quarrels continued between Rose and Arthur, until he finally agreed, and arranged a day that he and Roy could pay Mr Wigram a visit.

It was the following Monday. Roy had taken the day off work; he was excited to go with Arthur to see Mr Wigram. They drove along the winding roads towards Gloucester. When they arrived at the property, Arthur pulled the car up to the front of the large house. Arthur got out and asked Roy to wait in the car. Roy wound down the window to let in some air as it was a warm day. As he did a man appeared from the far side of the house. He walked towards the car and asked me what we were doing here. "Arthur has gone in to see you sir," Roy replied. The man then smiled and said, "No not me, he's gone in to speak with my father, he mentioned the appointment he had this morning." They started chatting and introduced themselves to one another.

Roy was talking with Neville, Mr Wigram's son. Roy could not imagine how old Mr Wigram must have been as his son looked a fair age. "You look like your father, have you ever met him?" Neville asked. "Met him? I've never seen a picture of him. I have no idea what he looks like." Neville invited Roy into the house to show him some photographs of Edward. Roy could hear Arthur talking. He and Mr Wigram came into the room. "I want to give Roy a picture of the Duke of Windsor, if that's alright?" Neville asked his father. Mr Wigram opened the cupboard and pulled out a box of black and white photos, pictures of King George and all the Royal Family. He sifted through them and then found some of Edward VIII. He handed them to Roy, explaining each of the uniforms he was wearing. Roy was excited to learn something new about his father and the uniforms he was wearing. Mr Wigram gave him two of the photographs to keep. Roy couldn't thank him enough for being so welcoming and kind to them. As they left, Arthur asked Mr Wigram to cover certain points of their conversation, "Cover everything you can in the letter, and send it to me. I would be very grateful, it's for the boy and his future." Mr Wigram agreed, shook Arthur's hand, and smiled at Roy and said goodbye.

Roy was excited all the way home, but Arthur hardly said a word. Roy treasured the photographs. He waited for the right moment to show them to his mother. When she finally saw them, she showed no emotion at all. She looked at Roy and said, "You need to let things go for now, let things settle with Arthur." Roy didn't argue as he was happy with what he had discovered.

**One of the photographs given to Roy by Mr Wigram.**
**Roy trimmed the photograph and carried it in his wallet.**

Years later he wrote on the back – *My Father Edward not Andrew*
*(Robert Andrew Powell – Known as Andrew to the Family)*

In 1956, Roy married Rosemary. On the morning of the wedding, Roy was asked to leave from the Maerdy. The same morning, he was given a large cardboard box. He opened it and inside was a Savile Row suit. It fitted like a glove. It was perfect. Roy thanked his mother, with a smile, she replied, "You need to look your best on your wedding day." The wedding went well, and Roy and Rosemary moved to the tied cottage at Blackbrook Farm. Roy often thought about his father and wanted to get in touch with him, but at this time it wasn't possible.

Just over 2 and a half years after they married, Rosemary found out she was pregnant. There were no complications and nine-months later, she gave birth to a baby girl, Sally. She was beautiful, Roy could not wait to take her to the Maerdy to introduce his daughter to his mother. When he showed her, Rose groaned, she wasn't interested with a granddaughter. Roy could see this upset Rosemary and decided to take her to see her parents as they would be most excited. Rosemary's family were thrilled to see them with the new baby. They had no problem having a girl for their first grandchild. They were just excited to have a grandchild and that Rosemary and Roy were happy.

The following week, Roy was at the Maerdy Farm helping Eric with the sheep. When they went in for lunch, Rose kept lecturing him about his choice of wife, and that he should have never married Rosemary. Not only did she have an illness, but she gave birth to a girl. Rose was still against having girls in the family, she only wanted boys. Rose said

"Roy, you should try again, have a boy." This upset him, he couldn't believe his mother's opinion of his wife and decided that he would stay away from the farm for a while.

The following years Roy and Rosemary had been trying for another child, but Rosemary had had several miscarriages.

They had both decided they wanted to have a farm of their own. Roy knew the only way this could happen was if he asked his mother if she would help, putting up half of the money to pay for it. Rose agreed to help, but if the farm was to be sold, for any reason, the money would have to be paid back to her. It took a long time but eventually a farm came up for sale. It was called The Grieg. It was on the hill above the Weir, heading away from Ewyas Harold, over the brook, along Prill road, and then keep straight on along Rabbit Lane. It was a bit of a climb up hill towards the property but that did not matter, they were excited to have it. Rosemary was in good health at this point and enjoyed helping Roy. They had large chicken sheds and she would help collect the eggs, getting them ready for sale. Roy also had started carrying out deliveries with his small van for the local grocer Warrens.

**Roy and Rosemary Wedding day 1956**
*Roy in his Savile Row suit*
Arthur and Rose on the left – Rose in her fur coat from David

**The Grieg Farm**

# Chapter 55

# IT'S A BOY

Nearly six years later, Rosemary, became pregnant again. She told Roy not to say anything to anyone until she knew that she could carry the baby longer than 12 weeks. The pregnancy was very draining on Rosemary's health, she was always tired and had no energy to do anything. She kept on with the housework but found it hard to help Roy with the chickens. Five months came and went, and the baby was doing fine during pregnancy, so they told everyone the news.

In May 1965, Rosemary gave birth to a boy, Robert Andrew. He was fine and healthy. They took him home to the farm and waited for Sally to come home from school. As Sally walked up the lane towards the house, she could see her mum and dad with her baby brother. They said to her "we finally have our son and heir." Roy could not wait to take the new baby to see his mother. The next morning, they all headed for the Maerdy farm. When Roy introduced the baby to his mother, she cooed over him. He found this very strange, such a different reaction between his two children. As Arthur came into the room, Rose slipped passed him leaving the room. He looked at the baby and shook Roy's hand with a large approving grin on his face. Rose was quickly back, and she handed Roy fifty pounds and told him to get the baby whatever he needed. Rose looked at Rosemary and with a genuine smile, she said, "Well done." Roy and Rosemary could not have been more pleased. After a short time, they went to visit Rosemary's family the Jones's, to show them their new son. They all congratulated them both and celebrated. It was one of the happiest days they have had for a long time.

Over the next few months Roy noticed Rosemary could not get over her tiredness, so he took her to the Doctor. The Doctor made an appointment for Rosemary to go and see a specialist in the hospital. They carried out a number of tests on her and told her that she needed to rest when she felt tired. Roy was finding it hard to manage everything on his own. His brother Jim would come up the hill from the Weir to help when he could, and Violet helped Rosemary around the house and with Sally. Everyone could see how much of a strain it was for Roy. The Maerdy now had a telephone of its own and Roy wanted to make contact with his father, Edward, to tell him he had a grandson. He spoke to Rose and Arthur and asked if there was any way he could contact him. Arthur went into his office and picked up a letter which contained many pages, he passed it to Roy. "It's what Mr Wigram sent to me, after that day we went to see him. I want you to have it." Rose went to her bedroom and brought down many letters to give to Roy. She said, "I think it would be best if you write to Edward first. He knows all about you, as I have kept in touch with him." Roy looked at Arthur, who, for the first time, was lost for words. Roy took the letters from both of them. He thanked them for the letters and made his way to the front door. He could not wait to get back home, and show then to Rosemary, they could read them together. As he left, he could hear his mum and Arthur going at one another, he got in his car and shut the door and drove off.

That evening, they read the letters together. The following day Roy wrote an informative letter to Edward, about his marriage to his beautiful wife Rosemary and their new baby son Robert Andrew. It took several weeks before he received the long-awaited reply. He read it over and over again, this was the first time his father had spoken to him, even if it was in written form. Roy then decided he would put pen to paper and write another letter, this time enclosing a photograph of his family. In his reply to this letter, Edward wrote how well they all looked, and did he like the suit he had sent to him for his wedding day. Roy was amazed as he did not think for one moment that his father had arranged for the suit to be made. Roy was not always sure what to write in a letter to Edward, so in his reply he asked if he could telephone him.

Several weeks went by and no letter came from Edward. Roy carried on with the farm and delivering groceries to the local community. Rosemary seemed more fatigued than usual and after having morning sickness, she believed she must be pregnant again. She was so pleased and loved the thought of having another child. Roy was worried and asked her to see the consultant at the hospital, but she refused and said that nature would take its course. She carried the baby well and another son was born, Michael. Both her and Roy were delighted as he was fine and healthy.

Weeks passed and Rosemary had an appointment with the Muscular Dystrophy Consultant. They confirmed that her muscles deterioration had progressed. Rosemary could now only walk for a short distance, with the aid of a stick. Further tests would be arranged for her and for the children, to see if they were carrying the muscle weakness. She needed sleep throughout the day and would often fall asleep in the chair, in front of the fire. Rosemary new that she would not be able to have any more children but was thankful that the three they had were perfect.

Roy – Rosemary – Robert Andrew

## Chapter 56

## IT'S FAMILY

Over the next three years, Roy found it hard to make money with the farm. Rosemary found it difficult to walk down to the village with the children and back up to the farm. Together they agreed they would sell the farm and move somewhere they could manage to live together. He went to the Maerdy and spoke about this to his mum, who was in favour, if it would help him. He asked her if she would mind him using their telephone, as he would like to ring his father in France. He had taken one of the last letters he had received from his father, as this had how to contact him. Rose could tell he was nervous and said she would speak to David first if he preferred that. He picked up the phone and spoke to the operator, "could you put me through to... in France" he said. It took a number of attempts before he was connected. Rose took the phone off Roy and, at first, a French person was speaking, Rose did not understand a word. She was then passed to a lady, who spoke English with a French accent, but she could not understand what Rose was asking for. Rose was asked many questions, and in the end, she raised her voice and said, "Tell David it is family. FAMILY!" She repeated it several times until a voice came to the telephone that she recognised. "It's Rose, Rose from York House. Is that you David?" She asked. He spoke to her for several minutes. Her voice changed from that strong woman into a young girl and Roy could see her blushing. "I have Roy here and he would like to speak with you." She eventually passed the phone to Roy. He could hardly get the words out as he was nervous, talking to his father for the first time. The voice on the other end of the telephone spoke slowly and clearly, as if he was thinking of every word he said. Roy had the feeling at the end of the call, that his father was happy to have heard from him, and they agreed to take another call the following week. They said their goodbyes and hung up. Roy looked to his mother who had a beaming smile as she could see how pleased Roy was. Roy said thank you to his mum for her help and headed for the door, "I must go now, as Rosemary will need help with the children." As he headed out the door his brothers came in and asked him if everything was all right. "Yes, things could not be better he said," and headed for the car. Roy drove home, singing in the car. He was so happy. He saw Rosemary and threw his arms around her with such excitement. He told her every detail of the conversation with his father and that he was looking forward to speaking to him again.

Two weeks later, Roy went to his mother's to use the phone again to call his father. He asked Edward if he would mind if they could travel to France to visit him, he could meet Rosemary and the children. David told him that sounded like a nice idea, he would love to meet his family. Roy went home to Rosemary and told her how they have the chance to go to France and to meet his father. They spoke all evening, planning their trip with the children, neither of them had been to France before. They speculated on where he lived and what he would be like towards them. Roy and Rosemary had had the discussion about selling the farm and moving to a suitable home. They both agreed that they would go to France first and then look for a new place to live. Over the next few days, Roy and Rosemary spoke of nothing else except going to France to meet his father. It was the be all and end all to everything. Roy thought it would change their lives forever.

A week later, Roy was standing in front of the farmhouse and could hear a car coming up the drive. It had rained a few days before, but on this hot sunny day, the track was drying out fast; when that happened, if you drove too fast, it would send a lot of dust into the air. He could hear the car hitting every pothole along the way. It came towards the house bouncing into the yard, and then, with an abrupt halt, the driver opened his door and rushed to the back door of the car. Roy thought they must be in the wrong place. A well-dressed man got out of the back of the car. He stood for a moment and then asked, "Powell. Are you Powell?" Roy was curious and hesitatingly replied, "I am. And you are?" The man stepped forward, "I am Mountbatten. Lord Mountbatten." Roy wondered why he said that twice and thought that he may have thought Roy was hard of hearing. Lord Mountbatten looked Roy up and down. Roy knew what he must be thinking, as he was stood there in front of Lord Mountbatten; wearing his old flannel trousers, a check shirt, and a pullover that Rosemary's aunty had knitted about five years earlier, that was stretched on one side from the kids pulling on it. Lord Mountbatten stood there in his immaculate three-piece suit, collar, and tie. "Can I help you?" Roy asked. Mountbatten replied, "I need to speak to you about the Duke of Windsor, shall we go inside?" Roy walked to the door and opened it. "We have a visitor, put the kettle on," he called out to Rosemary. Rosemary came into the kitchen. "This is…" before Roy could say who it was, Lord Mountbatten introduced himself, "Mountbatten. Lord Mountbatten." And shook Rosemary's hand. She offered him a cup of tea and with a smile, he said yes. Roy escorted him into the sitting room, it looked wonderful. The room had recently been painted and had a new three-piece suite. "Do you know who I am?"

Lord Mountbatten asked. Roy had no idea, he looked about seventy years old, spoke very well, but seemed to talk down to him. He told Roy stories of how he could fix things between him and the Duke of Windsor. Half of the time, Roy did not have a clue what he was on about. Roy could tell Lord Mountbatten did not like this. He asked so many questions and then after half an hour, Roy asked what he was doing there. "I hear you have spoken to the Duke of Windsor many times on the telephone, and you have been corresponding with him for a long time." "I have," Roy said, but was still uncertain of what Mountbatten wanted from him. He told me that Edward had removed some papers, after King George had granted the title to my dad, Arthur. He said he was trying to get that put right, so the title will be mine and then for my son, Robert Andrew." Lord Mountbatten asked if he could see the letters. Roy had no reason not to show them to him, as he was promising to take the letters and speak to the Queen. Roy gave Mountbatten the letters on the joint agreement and understanding that they would be returned to him. Once Mountbatten had finished his tea, he made his excuses to leave and got back into the car. Roy advised the driver which side of the lane to drive on, to avoid the potholes, but the driver took no notice. He took off at speed and hit all the potholes along the way, as he did on the way in.

It was the day Roy was to call his father, he had told Rose and Arthur of his visit from Lord Mountbatten. He was excited to tell his father of the visit too. When Roy called Edward, he was told that he was unavailable, and it would be best if he did not call again. Roy's heart sank. He told Rose and Arthur what he was told on the phone. "I think we all know why Mountbatten called by. He did not call to help sort anything out for me. He had called to take any evidence I had from my father, but little does he know, I did not give him all the letters. I still have several. Enough to prove who I am."

**Roy Albert**

**Robert Andrew**

Edward VIII          Robert Andrew